Equine Structural Integration:

Myofascial Release Manual

An Illustrated Guide to Increasing Equine Performance,
Balance and Movement

James V. Pascucci
Advanced Rolfer® (ACR), (NCTMB)

Sane Systems Press
Longmont, CO

ISBN 0-9790535-0-1
ISBN 978-09790535-0-4

Library of Congress Catalog Card No. 2006909701

Library of Congress Cataloging-In-Publication Data

Pascucci, James V., 1953-
        Equine Structural Integration: Myofascial Release Manual. An Illustrated Guide to
Increasing Equine Performance and Balanced Movement by James V. Pascucci
        p. cm
        Includes bibliographical references and index.
        ISBN 10: 0-9790535-0-1
        ISBN 13: 978-09790535-0-4
        1.Horses--Diseases--Alternative Treatment 2. Myofascial Pain Syndromes
        3. Manipulation--massage 4. Horsemanship

Acknowledgements

I would like to express my thanks to many of the people who have encouraged and helped me with this book. To Dr. Ida Rolf; without her development of Structural Integration (aka Rolfing®)—a sane way to help the body change—this book would not have happened. To my teachers at the Rolf Institute who taught me not only a way to make a living, but a way to help others. To Jim Asher and Ron Thompson, who taught me to "Rolf", and gave me the courage to reach out and teach others. To Tom Myers, who challenged me to define "Equine Rolfing", and encouraged me ten years ago to write a book on what I had developed (we'll get there with the next book Tom). To Liz Gaggini, who encouraged me to train as a Rolfer in the first place. For their editorial help, Lynn Wolf and Mary DeForest. For their proof reading of early chapters I want to thank Rachel Gosling, Sandy Collins and Morningstar. I want to thank Nick Pascucci for his photography and proof reading, and for being willing to go down to the barn with me even when he had other things to do. For her photography and her willingness to let me work with her horses, I want to thank my friend Carol Walker. I want to thank my wife Susan for being my sounding board, for putting up with long commutes so I could have horses at home, and for being my best friend.

There are so many horses that have—in their own way—taught me things: Dani, Yahalla, Rocky (aka Dark Crimson), Yves, Ziggy (aka Eden's Perlijah) and Zen (aka Agente Especial), all lent their bodies to my determining a way to integrate the equine structure. I want to thank the people who have taken my course and provided me the opportunity to test my ideas. Keep your clocks set on horse time! And last but not least, I want to thank my clients who have had enough trust in me to let me work with their horses.

Cover Photos by: Nick Pascucci

Interior Photographs by:

Carol Walker of Living Images (www.livingimagescjw.com):

MFR Techniques - All photos
Head Techniques - Figures 1-9
Neck Techniques - Figures 1- 5
Shoulder Techniques - Figures 1-8
Forearm Techniques - Figures 1-4
Rear Techniques - Figures 4-8
Scar Techniques - Figures 1-4
Myofascial Stretching - Figures 10-12

Nick Pascucci (www.JNNWebdesign.com):

What is Fascia - All photos
Equine Structure - All photos
Equine Movement - All photos
Safety - All photos
Head Techniques - Figures 10-15
Forearm Techniques - Figures 1-4
Rear Techniques - Figures 1-3 and 9-16
Myofascial Stretching - Figures 1-9

All illustrations by Jim Pascucci

Table of Contents

Safety

Fascial Release Techniques

Techniques for The Head

Table of Contents

Techniques for the Rear cont...

Techniques for Scars

Myofascial Stretching

Myofascial Stretching cont...

Table of Contents

Preface

In 1994 I finished my year long basic Rolfing training at the Rolf Institute of Structural Integration, the school started by Dr. Rolf. I had entered the school thinking I would limit my practice to horses. However, during my training I determined that I liked working with people and dogs as well as with horses.

When I investigated the current state of equine rolfing I found it to be less of a discipline than I had hoped. Rolfers were working with horses and doing what ever they thought needed to be done. There was no articulation of what this was. The few articles that were in the journals were lacking in any specificity. My colleagues' work with horses ranged from performing a traditional Rolfing ten series to what rolfers call "spot work", such as releasing a hamstring restriction.

I decided that I needed to use my knowledge of horses, rolfing and engineering to craft a way to work with the equine structure—the quadruped—in an orderly manner that would integrate it with gravity. A lofty goal.

The place I started was with the human ten session series developed by Dr. Rolf. It seemed logical that this series held the answer, if it was modified, to adapt it from its bipedal origins to fit the quadruped structure.

I went through the goals of the human ten series and determined which ones fit the quadruped. I then articulated a series of goals for the horse that would optimize its performance. (This was a further distinction; the goals for a horse are different than for a dog, even though they are both quadrupeds.) This meant a lot of reading, from dressage to Xenophon. It also meant looking at the mechanics of the horse, in standing and in movement (static and dynamic).

I set about using my two horses as my test subjects. I set up experiments, making a fascial change and measuring how long it lasted. (For instance if you release a hamstring and measure how long it takes for the hamstring to become hypertonic again, you can determine whether or not the hamstring is the primary or secondary problem.) I measured the relationship between body parts, angles of flexion and extension, rotations.... I designed devices to measure the rotation of a foot; to measure the effects of my work on toe-in and toe-out conformation. When I thought I had some concept figured out I went out and found horses to work with for free—except for photo and video rights—to get more data. (Being that the work was free I had a lot of takers, who were happy to be part of a study group.)

After more than a year of this experimentation I developed a five series for integrating the equine structure (later I developed one for canines).

Having been urged to start teaching this work by some of my teachers from the Rolf Institute, after my advanced training I started to teach this five series in workshops. This led to further refinements in the series and to an "advanced" workshop.

It is from the first part of the myofascial release workshop, that this book comes from. Before we can attempt to structurally integrate the horse we need to be able to release the horse's natural potential for change; we do this through fascial release.

Introduction

This is the first of two books that have their genesis in my adaptation of my training in human, bipedal, Rolfing Structural Integration to be used with the structure of quadrupeds—particularly horses. I use the word adaptation because I didn't simply take the bipedal structural integration and translate it; I created a methodology for working with the quadruped structure from what I had previously learned as a horseman, rolfer and engineer.

Fascia is known as the organ of form. It surrounds, defines and positions all of the organs, blood vessels, nerves, bones and muscles of the body to create the shapes we see in a body. Changes in fascia will be reflected in changes in the shape, or form of the body. This change may be small, effecting the functioning of blood vessels and nerves, or large effecting the locomotion of the entire body.

It only makes sense if we want to change the shape of a body that we would do so through the fascial system. There are two ways we could go about changing the body's fascia:

1. We could approach it directly, the subject of this book,

2. We could approach it indirectly, through the function of the body—as we see in a body changing shape due to exercise. The direct approach we are going to use is called *Myofascial Release.*

In this book the *tools* of the artist, so to speak, are presented along with some possible uses for these tools, the *techniques.* The use of these tools must be learned and practiced in order to move easily from *releasing the fascia* to *integrating it*—the subject of the second book.

It has been challenging to write a book that is useful to professional body therapists who are already working in the field as well as for lay people who want to be able perform some body therapy with the horses in their care. Over the last 10 years, I have had students in my classes who are advanced practitioners of some body therapy but not at all familiar with horses. I have also had students who knew very little about body therapy but were very knowledgeable about horses. Both have done equally well with facilitating change in the horses body-structure, using these techniques.

The danger, if you will, of writing a book about myofascial release, as a pre-cursor to book on structural integration, is that the reader may assume that the techniques presented are some rote methodology for working with the body—like a paint-by-numbers painting, where three is always yellow, and four is always blue. Unfortunately, this just doesn't happen in the living body—where change itself is the medium we are engaging. Using these techniques with a living body requires us to listen to it and adapt our therapeutic intervention as the changes occur. This is not about the application of a set number of strokes, in a certain direction, at a certain depth. It is about being present and working with the body, as well as being familiar with the tools and using them at the appropriate time.

Another potential difficulty with a book of *techniques* is that it can contribute to our believing that there are parts to the body that we can work with in isolation. If we see the body as being made up of parts, then making that part perform better could become our objective. However the body is a whole, not a collection of parts and, as such, we need to keep the view of the whole as we work.

We have to have a systems view of the body; if only because the lesions, restrictions and problems we are helping to address show themselves as a partitioning of the whole and it is with a systems view that we can integrate them back into the whole. We have to be able to move from the view of

working on a part (the shoulder for instance) to the view of bringing that part's function back into the optimal contribution to the whole.

To reduce the tendency to see the labeled parts of the body as separate entities (bones, tendons, shoulders, feet) I have kept the illustrations more general than a typical anatomy book, with their clean lines and distinct separations. By doing this I am hoping to encourage you to look for these concepts in the world at large. For instance how does the concept of *entrainment* exhibit itself in a band of horses walking in lock step? How does the concept of *organizing force* reveal itself in a flight of geese? When we can see these concepts as naturally occurring phenomena we can trust in our ability to experience and make use of them in our work with horses.

In keeping with this idea, the first chapter of the book is about palpation. The work of myofascial release begins with the ability to sense the fascia. We release what we feel with our hands after being directed there by our hands and other senses. Without the ability to actually *feel* the body, having an anatomical label for what is under your hands is a useless mental exercise. To achieve mastery in this work we must be engaged in the ongoing enterprise of developing our sensory and palpatory literacy.

After we can sense and feel the fascia, it is important to understand its physiology. Having some understanding of the physiology helps us to better visualize the chain of events that occur in a fascial change; whether it is a positive therapeutic release of a restriction or the negative formulation of one.

Using a carpenter's tools as an analogy, we have to know something about nails and screws the carpenter's tools work on before we can successfully use them; the same is true with fascial release, we need to recognize the object (palpation) and know how they interact (physiology) before we can completely address them.

To be able to communicate with the client we need to speak the same language, otherwise we risk working *on* them and not *with* them. The chapter on the horse provides an introduction to the language of horses which is a non-verbal body language.

The chapter on movement provides an introduction to movement as it is used by the body to describe its *integration*. Movement—too much or too little— is the first signal to us that the horse's body is not integrated. (We might see this lack of integration as a short stride, or in the extreme it could show up as lameness.) From watching movement we develop a strategy for how we will work with the horse's fascia.

The last part of the book is about how to perform myofascial release with the horse. The chapter on safety covers setting up a safe environment for you and the horse. The technique introduction helps to familiarize you with the terminology as well as how each technique is performed. Finally we look at how we could use the techniques in working with different areas of the body.

This is where the danger of thinking there is a rote method for working can come about. This area of the book is presented to you as a series of possibilities not as rules. Dr. Ida Rolf, in suggesting that we should not get attached to a particular way of working said "If at first you don't succeed. Get the heck out." I would like to encourage you to follow this advice. If the technique you are using is not working abandon it and use another. Or go to another place in the body to work. (Fascia is a web and as such restrictions in one area can transmit their strain far into the web.)

To support you in using this book and understanding these concepts, I have setup an area on the website **www.equinesi.com** that will further address some of the concepts presented here. (Go to the book page and look for the book support button. This will direct you to a page with flash animations, some videos, articles and more illustrations.) I have also set up a discussion group on Yahoo, to subscribe to it, use this link **equinemyofascialrelease-subscribe@yahoogroups.com.**

I am very interested in your feedback on this book; it will help me make the next one better. Please feel free to contact me at **jim@equinesi.com**, with your comments. I appreciate it.

If you find this book and the work it describes useful and would like to continue your training, we would love to have you come to Colorado and attend one of the workshops. Also we can talk about bringing a workshop to your area.

Finally, please accept my sincere thanks for your purchase of this book. I hope you find it useful.

Chapter Contents

Palpation

Palpation

The act of touching tissue and that of palpating tissue are two different actions. Touch can be something simple like petting your cat. It can also have more of a therapeutic intention to it, such as helping the tissue change.

Palpation, on the other hand, is the gathering of information from all of the senses (touch is only one sense we use). Palpation is the reception of information from the "whole body" when we look at it, hear it, touch and smell it. (I left out taste, since I don't use that one too often when working.) We palpate from the tissue level to the cellular and energetic levels of the body.

When we observe the horse move (discussed in later chapters) we use our ears as well as our eyes, to palpate the horse from a distance. (Listening to the sounds of the foot falls of the horse can clue us in to a foot that is being weighted less than the others. It will sound hollow.)

For this discussion I am going to focus on the touch aspect of palpation. In other sections we'll talk about observing the horse move. I trust that you will use all of your senses to *palpate* your horses or those of your clients.

Palpation as a Guide

The information that we receive from palpation is used to determine the best treatment options. Some of the tissue attributes we can detect through palpation are:

Skin tension differences—Is the skin tighter or looser over a specific area? This can be determined through touch and sight.

Temperature differences—Is there more or less heat in the tissue than in the surrounding area?

Tenderness—Is the area more tender to the touch? How much?

Edema—Does the area have the boggy feel of *edema*?

Fibrosis or Scarring—How organized do the tissue fibers feel? Do they move in all directions?

Mobility/Motility—Is the tissue easy to move in all directions, *mobility*? Is there an inherent motion in the tissue, *motility*?

The three rhythms: Cranial, Respiratory and Cardiac. (There is more about this later.)

The above tissue attributes can be normal, such as loose hydrated skin in the neck. Or abnormal, skin that doesn't easily move in the back.

They can also be combined in such a way that they are normal when accompanying other changes, such as tight skin when part of a scar. Or abnormal when missing in a scenario, such as edema without heat—which may indicate trapped fluid.

Palpation gives us clues to a puzzle that we trying to solve.

The Palpation Sequence

The palpation sequence has three stages: detection, awareness (also called amplification) and concept of what was detected (also called interpretation). These three stages can be independently honed as a skill in their own right.

Each of these three stages feeds into the development of the strategy for the particular session as well as your current therapeutic intervention or stroke. As your palpation skills change, become more focussed, more aware, more informed, so will your strategies and interventions. They will become more refined and focussed and require less effort.

Detection—the skill of detection comes from knowing what to expect when the tissue is normal, so you can determine when something is abnormal. Like Colombo, the famous TV detective, we need to be able to tell when the tissue

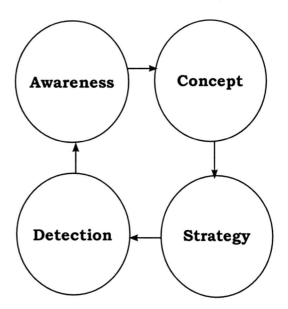

Figure 1. *Continually looping through the stages of palpation brings our work to life.*

is acting suspicious and not presenting the way it should. For example, is this heat I feel normal or abnormal for this area of the body? The more we have an understanding of what is normal, the better we'll be able to detect what is abnormal. This understanding comes from the academic study of anatomy and physiology and from touching horses or other beings.

Awareness—this is the ability to concentrate your palpation to make some sense of what you are experiencing, while at the same time becoming more cognisant of what your senses are reporting. At

Palpation is a continual journey of discovery and letting go of the discovery.

At first we think that we can't sense what we need to, to do this work. Our senses don't seem to speak the language that we need them to speak to communicate with the tissue. Then we think we've got it. We have to let go of this knowing something to make room for more experience. I think that a certain amount of uncertainty in our experience is needed to actually be available to the "freshness" of the experience. Being willing to stay with the uncertainty gives our work the vitality required to help suggest a change to the tissue.

this stage there's no descriptive label associated with the sensation; it is more of a "AHA that's something!". As you start to hone in on the sensation, you are able to disregard the extraneous information you are getting. With experience, what is and isn't extraneous information becomes more ingrained into our palpation, thus increasing *Palpatory Literacy.*

Conceptualization—at this level the sense perception is replaced with a mental model of what you are experiencing. This is both a benefit and liability. The benefit is that you can start to enter into the intervention phase, having decided what it is you're working with. The liability is the tendency to become blind to what you are experiencing based on your modality, training and ability to keep an open mind. For instance, you may think that everything you feel has to have MFR as an intervention. What you *believe* will condition what you *sense.* Leon Chaitow speaks to this: *" It is all too easy for the practitioner (even those with wide experience) to feel what she 'wants' to feel, or what she expects to feel. A relative degree of detachment from the process of assessment is therefore helpful, if not essential."*[1]

Strategy—The information gained from palpation feeds the development of the strategy of the intervention you'll make. It is this continuing process of palpation feeding strategy that brings your work to life and separates it from a learned routine that is applied by rote. **Figure 1.**

Learning Palpation

Bringing all of our senses into our palpation will increase our ability to accurately sense wholistically. When we are not using all of our senses, there is no possibility of consensus amongst them and we are sometimes confused by our experiences. We could think that a rope on the floor of a dark room is snake. But when the lights come on, allowing us to better use our sight sense, we see that it's simply a rope.

Try this exercise with a friend to see what I mean. It creates an environment where you aren't able to *direct* your sense of touch.

Exercise 1: Close your eyes and have a partner take an object, small enough to fit your hand, and rub your hand and fingers with it. You should remain passive. Let your friend decide how much information you should get from the object by moving it over your fingers, palm, etc., and by moving different parts of the object over your hand. They are in control of how much tactile information you will receive. You are not able to direct your sense of touch.

Take about 30 seconds for this and then, with your eyes still closed, guess what you think the object is.

Now have your friend put the object in your hand so you can touch it at will, directing your sense of touch. How long did it take you to determine what the object was? Was the second time shorter? Why?

This exercise, hopefully, pointed out that when you are passive in the palpation—with your friend deciding on the important information you receive—you aren't as easily able to discern what you've experienced. When you are more actively participating—using your own hands to move through the palpation loop—you can more readily conceptualize the touch information into a decision of what the object is.

This also holds true for the client we are working with. If they are passive to our touch or in the session, then they are less likely to understand what it is we are asking from them.

The horse will show its active engagement through movement during the session. This may seem like a contradiction, but I want the horse I am working with to be moving their body, participating and making sense of what I am asking of them as I help them release their fascia. I don't want them to stand perfectly still and falling asleep. In this latter case I am doing something to the horse, while in the former we are working together to affect a change. This, former way, of working will create a longer lasting change.

Exercise 2: Have your friend place a coin under a magazine. (You may want to start with a thin magazine and a big coin). Try and find the coin by feeling through the top of the magazine.

While you are doing this exercise, pay attention to what is happening in your mind. Are you anxious? Are you calculating where the coin may be? Do you notice that you find the coin more easily when you actually stop *doing*?

Exercise 3: Put a number of different objects with different shapes and textures into a box. (You could put different types of cloth, such as silk, corduroy, denim, or wool to add texture to thee exercise.) Have someone tell you what to find or make a list for yourself, if you're practicing alone. Then, without looking, find the objects.

Pay attention to the mental conversation you have with yourself as you move through the sensations you are having to find your object. Does it match the process described in **Figure 1?**

Exercise 4: This a variation on exercise 3. Put out a number of bowls with ice, oil, water, warm water, butter, yogurt…. You get the idea. Without looking, move through the bowls while *feeling* the contents. What is the difference between warm and cold? What is the difference between warm and cold water? What is the difference between oil and yogurt, or whatever? This is an exercise in building our palpation vocabulary.

At times, while working on a body, you'll feel something that has a fluid feel but it's more turgid than water. Being able to discriminate this feeling will influence your intervention strategy and the touch—depth, speed—you'll apply.

Pressure versus Depth

Many times in my work and in my teaching I'm asked the question: "How much pressure are you using?". There is a common misconception that the pressure one uses will determine the depth you are working.

In reality what determines the depth one works is: the *speed* that you use to approach the tissue, your *intention* as well as the *pressure.*

If you quickly press hard on the tissue, you risk creating a reflex arc that will hold you out of the body. (This is often mistaken for pain by people palpating too quickly. It's actually more of a *muscle spindle fiber* reaction.) You'll end up fighting the tissue at the level of the reflex, thinking you should be pushing harder and getting nowhere.

If you don't use enough pressure to overcome the dispersing of the energy by the hide, the fat and the fascia, you won't be able to get enough energy to the area to affect change at the depth you want. You have to balance speed with pressure—while actually working through the tissue—to get the change you want to achieve.

The other item that determines your depth, is your *intention*. Your intention is simply what you hold in your mind as your objective for that particular touch. If you have strong intention to work with bone then you'll be working with bone even with a light touch. Your intention will work as long as you can maintain complete contact with the horse. This method takes longer to affect change in the tissue, if only because it is more subtle.

There is also a point where—if you wait long enough—you'll feel the *entrainment* of the tissue to your touch and you'll be affecting deeper levels without increasing the pressure. This, however, can take a long time, and the horse may not stand still long enough for it to happen.

> *Entrainment sounds really exotic, but it happens all the time. The next time you can watch horses coming in from pasture at a walk, notice how they are in step with each other. This is a natural entrainment.*
>
> *In the tissue it is the cells actually lining up with your intention, entraining with you.*

The following exercise will help illustrate these concepts:

Exercise 5: In this exercise you will use your intention to palpate different tissue depths.

Write on three pieces of paper: bone, skin, myofascia, muscle and cranial rhythm, for instance. These are the depths you'll palpate; of course, you could make up more.

If you have three people available, one will be the palpator, one will the palpated and one will be the guide. If you don't have three people than use the written clues as the guide.

Have the palpated sit down on a chair facing the palpator. The palpator puts their hands on the palpated's thighs. (Both hands, both thighs.)

The palpator's intention is to palpate, skin, muscle, bone. Have the third person (or put the list of intentions under the chair where the palpated person can't see it) determine what order the palpator will palpate the desired tissue. The directions should be given without the palpated person seeing or hearing them.

Without unduly increasing your hand pressure, try using your intention to feel the tissue you want. When you are sure you've felt it, take your hands off and start again, moving on to the next item on the list.

The person receiving the touch should keep track of what they feel you are touching, and report to you later. "First it felt like bone."

Don't make it too complicated and don't make too much out of your success or lack of success. It doesn't mean that you have super duper intention if the palpated person felt you at the skin, bone, etc. The end result is not as important as the practice is.

It's more important to gain some understanding of how your body and mind work when you are working on differing levels of tissue. Do you tense up at the skin or bone level? Do you have a need to push hard to get to that muscle level? Can you drop your agenda and let what happens in the tissue happen?

To complete the experience switch places with the palpator and be palpated by them. It helps us understand our touch by

If you are working with a horse that is very reactive to your touch, you may want to resort to using more of your intention and entrainment. This takes longer to effect change but the level of awareness that is required, on your part, will often calm the horse as it senses you being more aware. Awareness is one of the characteristics of the leader of the herd, your possessing it puts you in a leadership and trust position with the horse.

experiencing the touch of another.

The Three Rhythms

There are three separate rhythms or pulsations in the body. We need to be aware of them because they are useful in telling us how the body is doing and they are a way to guide the rhythm of our work with the tissue. They are:

Cranial—the cranial rhythm is the oldest movement in the body, therefore the most primal. It starts when the fetus is a primitive brain and spinal cord, or *notochord*. Its origins are in the pulsations of the cerebral spinal fluid from the brain to the sacrum. (You may have heard of *Cranio-sacral* Therapy that works with this rhythm.)

Cardiac—the cardiac rhythm is what you think it is—the beating of the heart. This is the second oldest rhythm in the body. It also starts in utero.

Respiratory—is the function of breathing. The respiratory rhythm is the latest rhythm—not starting until after the horse is born.

Each of these rhythms contributes to the inherent motion that is found in the tissue at rest. This motion is called *motility*[2]. (See accompanying box.)

The motility caused by the cranial rhythm or pulse is very slight, that caused by the cardiac rhythm is a little larger and that caused by the respiratory rhythm is the largest.

It is relatively easy to see and feel the movement due to the respiratory rhythm, the body breathing, while the others are more subtle.

Working to these rhythms, when you can monitor them, will help you to facilitate a change in the horse that is easier to arrive at and longer lasting. These rhythms are a gateway into the nervous system's control over the tissue.

Before you start to palpate the client horse for the first time, you may want to stand back and look at the body to see if you can become aware of the breath moving through the tissue. If not, you at least want to assure that the horse is breathing!

Exercise 6: This exercise requires a partner. (It doesn't have to be a human; your horse, dog or cat will work fine.) You'll

> *Motility is the movement that is inherent in the tissue. When you push on skin it will have an inherent motility if it is healthy.*
>
> *The Motility will be reduced if it is de-hydrated.*
>
> *Mobility is the movement of the tissue either voluntarily or through the action of another system.*
>
> *One could argue that the definition of motility that I'm using is wrong, since this motion is coming from the brain, heart and respiratory diaphragm and fits the definition for mobility.*
>
> *I'm going to stick with my definition to separate it from the voluntary movement that the tissue undergoes in normal locomotion—since the motility is not voluntary.*

palpate these three rhythms with them. As stated before, each of the three rhythms has an effect on the tissue. (This effect is both distinct as well as combined.) The cranial rhythm is most readily palpated at the extremities, the limbs, because of the lever arm effect they provide.

In this part of the exercise you will be feeling the cranial rhythm by sensing the motion of the hair on the arm as it moves under your fingers.

To feel the cranial rhythm have your partner lie down somewhere comfortable for both you and them. Take your hand and gently put it over their bare arm. You want the palm of your hand to make gentle contact with the hair on their arm. (You can't do this through clothing since the arm doesn't always move the clothes.)

As the two of you relax into this feeling position, you will notice that their arm hair is moving, very slowly, under your palm. The hair will move one way, stop for a while and then move the other way. This back and forth movement is the cranial rhythm or pulse. It has a frequency of 8-12 cycles per second. These cycles are not always even, i.e. the hair may feel like it moves further in one direction than the other and the time between each change in direction may not be the same.

To palpate the cardiac rhythm you can gently lay your hand on your partner's tissue anywhere there's blood flow. You should feel the subtle movement of the blood through the tissue.

The respiratory rhythm is felt in the same way as the cardiac. You should feel the tissue relax with the exhale and become a little more tense with the inhale. This is not just the movement tensing the chest pulling the tissue tighter; the tissue will actually relax with the exhale. This is something you'll want to remember for your bag of tricks. You can coordinate your work with the respiratory rhythm to make it easier on the client and you.

These three *rhythms* are always available and moving in the living body. The ease with which they are able to move with and through the tissue is a sure sign of the health and integration of that tissue.

Spend some time sensing these three and exploring how they relate to each other as well as their general qualities. Are they always the same? Are they uniform in their in/pause/out movement? Does the heart sometimes beat faster or slower?

Does the in breath take longer than the out? Pay attention to your own rhythms; can you sense them? If you can, do you notice any entrainment or synchronization with your palpation partner as you work together?

Doing this will add to your repertoire of known sensations that you can use when working with the horse.

Tonus

The intact nervous system is constantly monitoring what is happening in the periphery of the body. The senses report to the Central Nervous System (CNS) about the world, and the CNS is sending control information back in response to the sensed world.

This constant feedback loop provides a certain amount of *charge* to the system to assure it is primed to react to a real or imagined threat. This charge is called *tone* or *tonus*. The healthy body system, is neither too charged up, *hypertonic*, or too loose, *hypotonic*.

When we press on the tissue, we will feel a certain amount of pushing back or resistance from the tissue. This is the tonus. This almost instantaneous response to our pressing occurred because of the tone.

On a toned body, the tissue doesn't collapse under our hands when we touch it. This is because the tissue tone keeps us outside. We also don't push on a toned body and bounce off of it. If the tissue tone is hypotonic we don't experience the push back and if it's hypertonic the push back will be too strong. Somewhere in between, not too tight and not too loose is healthy body tone.

In order to work at any depth, other than the hide, we need to work with the tonus in a non-threatening way for the CNS to allow us into the tissue. This is the reason that we use a slow approach with the tissue. This slow approach accommodates the nervous system to assure it that our touch is not a threat and, as such, it can let us in deeper and deeper.

The tone of the tissue determines

I don't think you can do this exercise with yourself as the subject of the palpation. The reason is that the feedback loop is internal to your body and will constantly change.
That said, you can feel your own tissue and get a sense of where it is too tight or too loose.

how fast or slow we must work to influence a change in it. If there is a lot of tone, the body feels like a trampoline and we'll bounce out if we work too fast.

If there is little tonus, we can sink in faster, but need to be careful not to do any damage since the natural tonal protection is low.

In some cases, especially in *Structural Integration,* to balance the body, we will want to reduce tonus in one place while increasing it in another.

Exercise 7: You don't need a human partner for this exercise; if you have a horse, use it. A cat or a dog work equally well. Try and stay with a mammal though.

With a partner, palpate different parts of their body and feel the spring or bounce back in their tissue. This will not be the same in all areas of the body. It should feel the same for corresponding body areas, so palpate sides and compare them.

End Feel

One of the hardest palpatory sensations for people to understand is what is called *end feel.* This is the feeling of the tissue at some distance to where you are actually touching the body. It is commonly referred to when working with a joint or across joints.

We experience it all the time, if we ride a bicycle or drive a car. It's that *feel* of the road in the handle bars or steering wheel.

This last exercise is one that you can do while driving or riding your bike. As you are driving, feel the texture of the road through the car or bike. See if you can drive over a crack in the road and feel it in your hands. That is exactly what we call, *end feel.*

Endnotes

1. Chaitow, L 1997 Palpation Skills, Assessment and Diagnosis Through Touch. Churchill Livingstone, New York.

2. Barral, J 1998 Visceral Manipulation. Eastland Press, Seattle Washington.

Contents

Fascia

What is Fascia?

Fascia

If we could remove all the skin, muscle, bones, nerves, veins, arteries and organs—everything but the *fascia*—from the equine body, we would end up with a form that resembles a *cotton candy* version of the original animal. We would be able to see through the fascial weave since there is space between the layers of fascia, making it translucent. The places where we removed the muscles, bones, nerves, veins, arteries and organs would look like spider web *pockets or pouches* holding the shape of the removed tissue.

One of my colleagues did exactly this type of extraction—as described above—with an MRI Data set of a human thigh from the National Institute of Health. He used a computer program to remove all data that is not associated with fascia from the MRI image. What is left is an image of the web like containers created by fascia. It is obvious that one is looking at a thigh cross section, what is impressive is the extent to which fascia defines the body and is truly the organ of form.

There would be uniformity in the density of the fascia, except at the places were strain from unbalanced riding, ill-fitting equipment, shoeing problems or trauma was evident. In these areas the fascia would be thicker and the layers may be stuck together, dehydrated and not moving independently. The greater the impact of these stressors the greater the thickening of the fascia would be, as the adaptation to the stress required more fascial material[1]. Some of these thicker areas could impinge upon the space or pocket that contains a muscle or nerve, restricting their normal function, pulling on them, twisting them out of their normal shape. While it may appear that these thickenings are abnormal, they're not. This thickening or re-enforcing is the normal response of fascia to strain placed upon it; it is the *healthy* response of this living tissue which seeks to return to *homeostasis*. The thickening is the body's way of supporting the area under strain and will be proportionate to the strain.

From Cell to Fascial Matrix

Connective tissue (CT) is one of the most prolific tissues in the body (blood is a connective tissue). As the name implies, it functions to connect or network together other tissue types and to provide a framework or scaffolding for the cells of these other tissue types to lay down their product.

Fascia is a type of connective tissue that is composed of varying amounts of *collagen, elastin,* and *reticular* fibers suspended within a *ground substance* made up of *proteoglycans and water.* The collagen gives the fascia its tensile strength while the elastin gives it its elasticity. Depending upon the mix of these two main fibers, the fascia can be considered to be extensible, as in the muscle's myofascia, or have more tensile strength, as in a tendon. The reticular fibers are found where some supporting structure or framework is needed without the strength of collagen, such as the walls of veins. *Fibroblast* and *reticular cells* are responsible for providing the building blocks from which collagen, elastin and reticular fibers are formed in the *Extra Cellular Matrix* (ECM). The ECM is the environment outside

These same fibroblast and reticular cells can change their output and become chondrocytes providing the building blocks for the cartilage of joints.

Cartilage is another type of connective tissue.

Fiber Type	Produced By	Function
Collagen	Fibroblasts	Tensile Strength
Elastin	Fibroblasts	Elasticity
Reticular	Reticular Cells	Binding Factor
Ground Substance	H2O, GAGs	Separate/ Lubricate

Table 1 *The connective tissue cells produce the fibers that make up fascia. In the case of the ground substance it is not produced by any cell but is made up of H2O and GAGs, bound collagen, elastin and reticular fibers.*

the Fibroblast and Reticular cells, while the intercellular environment is inside the cells.

Table 1, lists the functions of the various cells found in fascia.

Within the fibroblasts' intercellular environment, a triple helix chain of amino acids is produced, which is known as *procollagen.* These amino acid chains are bound together by *intra*molecular cross links which are very stable. The procollagen is released by the fibroblasts into the Extra Cellular Matrix (ECM) where they bind together through *intra*cellular cross links to form *Tropocollagen.* (Don't confuse *intra* with *inter* cellular.) These intracellular links arc initially fairly weak becoming stronger with time.

Intramolecular
Cross links

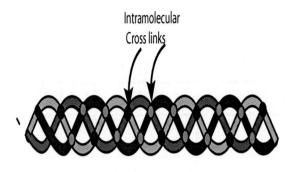

Figure 1 *A triple helix Procollagen molecule is released by the Fibroblasts into the ECM. This production is mediated by the tension the Fibroblast experiences.*

(This is one reason why fascial release is contra-indicated in the early phases of some traumas, such as a laceration. It could disrupt these links.) **Figure 1.**

The tropocollagen combines with other tropocollagen strands to make up *microfibrils,* which in turn group together to form *fibrils* and then once again to form *fibers* of collagen. It is at the level of the fibers of collagen that we are working when we use fascial release techniques. **Figure 2**

The collagen, elastin and reticular fibers provide the structural framework of the fascial matrix. W*ater* and

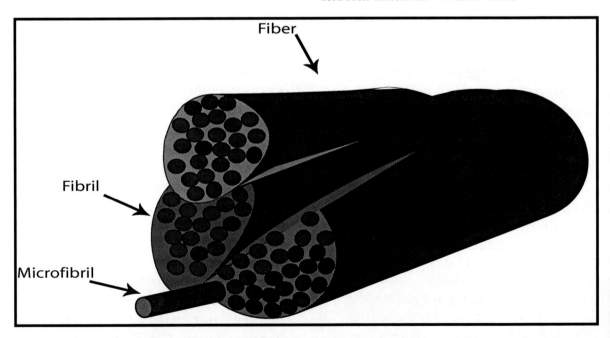

Figure 2 *The Tropocollagen combines to make up a Microfibril which combines to make up a Fibril. The Fibrils further combine to make up a Fiber.*

Figure 3 *Just as the rain water is caught in this spider web in the grass, the collagen and elastin fibers act to contain the hydrophilic GAGs which will swell with water. If the containment of the collagen and elastin is broken, as in an injury, the GAGs will swell out of control. This is what we see when there is a swelling injury.*

glucosaminoglycans (GAGs) attached to a protein (this combination is now called a *proteoglycan*) provide space between the structural fibers as well as lubricate these fibers, allowing adjacent collagen units to slide across each other. GAGs are *hydrophilic*, which means that they attract and bind with water. The hydrophilic GAGs swell with water but are contained by the collagen and elastin fibers, like a fibrous net containing a balloon of water. If there is any disruption to the fibrous container, the GAGs will swell with water beyond the containment. This is what we see

A very important GAG is Hyaluronic Acid (HA). You may know of a horse that has had an HA injection. The Hyaluronic Acid acts as a pre-cursor to the development of synovial fluid by the joint's synovium tissue.

Synovial joints are arthrotic joints, they have a hyaline cartilage on their articulating surfaces which depends on synovial fluid as a lubricant.

Synovial fluid is produced by a specialized cells in the synovium, these cells can change into chondrocytes to produce cartilage when needed to repair the joint cartilage.

in a swelling injury. In an injury with swelling, the collagen and elastin have been damaged and are unable to contain the GAGs which continue to bloat with water.

An analogy of what happens in the soft tissue is depicted in **Figure 3,** water contained in a spider web. The web acts as a container for the water droplets.

Organ of Form

Fascia is known as the *organ of form* and is a three dimensional web that surrounds and defines the shape of everything in the body: nerves, bone, arteries, veins, muscles as well as the visceral organs. In fact, you can recognize a body part because the fascia gives it form. Everything in the body is organized spatially by its position within this web-like fascial network.

This unified nature of fascia means that the entire body is inter-connected from the top of the head to the bottom of the feet and from the deepest bone marrow to the skin. The fibers are like the fibers in a woven cloth. Similar to cloth, because of its connectivity, the fascia will transfer strain from one part of the body to locations that are more distant in the body. This is both a benefit and a problem: The benefit comes from

the distribution of the strain to more than one portion of the fascial matrix which works to prevent an overload. The problem comes when the strain reflects a disturbance somewhere far removed from the strain itself and the therapist chases the symptom rather than the cause.

Fibroblasts react to mechanical forces by producing more procollagen (collagen bound to a protein). It has been shown that fibroblasts sense strains in their environment[1], the ECM, and produce the appropriate amount of collagen, elastin or reticular fibers for the strain.

While under strain the fascial fibroblasts will line up along the line of strain, laying down their product (collagen, elastin and reticular fibers). The fibroblasts react to a strain by producing more product to accommodate the need to resist the strain. If a large strain is detected then more collagen than elastin will be laid down. For a small strain more reticular fibers may be used.

When one part of the fascial network is injured or strained in any way, the effects can be experienced far from that local site[2], transmitted along what could be described as *fascial meridians*[3].

Transference of strain is depicted in **Figure 4**, a T-shirt hanging on a branch, in which the strain nervous system adaptation[4].

When the nervous system adapts to the strain pattern, the movement algorithm, regulated by the nervous system, is altered to find the path of least resistance to accommodate the strain pattern. This new aberrant movement pattern can lead to a training problem later in the horse's career that may erroneously be attributed to some more recent issue.

Fascia, as the organ of form has to be able to change shape

All voluntary movements in the body are learned movements. The nervous system develops a complicated algorithm—made up of smaller movements—to control the movement. When there is a long standing strain pattern this algorithm may change, with the result that the horse has seemed to forget how to do a particular movement or is not capable of moving ahead in its training.

Figure 4 *The fascial network distributes strain much like the fabric of this shirt is showing the strain imparted to it by the branch it is hanging on. The tension in the bent branch is reflected in the fabric.*

imparted to the shirt by the branch, is reflected in the fabric far from the actual branch. If this strain were long lasting, such as a postural or conformational problem, the fascial network would change as the fibroblasts laid down collagen and elastin molecules along the strain's path. (This happens as the body builds up this strained area to strengthen it in working with the increased force of the strain. The strain can happen from something as simple as the shifting its body weight to avoid the pain of a rider out of balance or moving the weight off a shod foot a *hot* nail.) This strain pattern could eventually be incorporated into the fascial *weave* and would result in a

to meet specific tissue needs for both strength and to accommodate complicated movement. (The fascia has to be able to change shape and return to the original shape, i.e. the lungs expanding and relaxing).

The particular requirements for

Movement	Twisting	Bending	Elongation	Compression	Shearing
Ligament	X	X			X
Tendon	X	X			
Myofascia	X	X	X	X	
Skin	X	X	X	X	X

Table 2 *The collagen and elastin mixture of the different parts of the body accommodates the types of stresses that the part's tissue experiences. Ligaments have to be able to twist, bend and resist shear, and then return to the original form.*

movement will be reflected in the organization of the fascia for that body area. While the fascia making up a tendon will have collagen and elastin fibers lined parallel to each other, to accommodate a direct pulling strain and the need for strength (tendons can hold approximately 2000 lbs./square inch). A ligament's collagen and elastin will be more diagonally oriented to accommodate the twisting experienced by ligaments at joints. See **Table 2**.

I want to emphasize that both of these actions, laying down the supporting tissue and moving along the strain pattern, are a natural healthy response of the fascia and nervous system to sustained strain. It is not disease but rather, as Dr. Rolf called it, *dis-ease,* a lack of tissue ease. This lack of ease becomes problematic over time in that it causes the body to use an inefficient movement pattern that result in balance issues. Our

work with the tissue, through myofascial release, will return it to a *homeostatic* point of ease.

The Gel/Sol Relationship

The medium that the collagen, elastin and reticular fibers are deposited in is called *ground substance*. Water makes up 70% of the ground substance and the collagen, elastin and reticular fibers, make up the remaining 30%[5]. Ground substance has the ability to change from a *gelatinous* (gel) state to a *solute* (sol) state when under sustained pressure. It is the ability of fascia to change state—from gel to sol—that is the working basis of myofascial release.

This sustained pressure could come from movement of the tissue as the body moves (as in stretching) or from the application of pressure from the therapist's hands in myofascial release therapy. In its *gel* state—this is the more solid of the two states—the ground substance disperses trauma and helps the body to maintain a more rigid shape[6]. When the ground substance is in the *sol* state— the less solid—it is lubricating the fascial layers allowing them to slide with respect to each other rather than creating cross links and adhering to each other.

The ground substance is a crystalline structure and is *piezoelectric*[7] in that it responds to pressure by changing its shape while producing an electromagnetic charge. This is neither an unusual event in the equine body nor in the natural world. Through the application of a mechanical force or stretch, we can cause the ground substance to make a *phase change* from a *gel* to a *sol*.[8,9] This change is called *thixotropy*.

In the sol state a sustained pressure or stretch can cause the collagen fibers to:

1) re-organize along the line of strain/stretch

2) allow more hydration in the tissue to occur, and

3) force the collagen adhesions (the hydrostatic cross links)[10] to release.

This pressure has to be sustained for some minimum time, 90 seconds or so, for the thixotropy to occur, which accounts for the reason why most massage—

consisting of the application of faster strokes—does not greatly influence the fascia. However, this 90 seconds is more of a guideline than a rule; follow and trust what you feel under your hands when deciding if there is a change occurring, not your watch.

Adaptation to Injury

When fascia is traumatized, for example, by a horse falling or being kicked, the fascial web may be damaged and not able to contain the hydrophilic GAGs. This allows the GAGs to swell with water beyond the containment, resulting in tissue swelling. The fibroblasts will heal this injury by producing more procollagen and releasing it into the ECM, which results in the creation of more collagen and elastin fibers to fill the break.

Because the newly formed Tropocollagen will have immature and weak cross links they are easy to disrupt. (As such, fascial release work is contra-indicated on recent injuries to allow the fascia time to heal.) Initially, the new collagen and elastin fibers will be irregularly arranged and randomly formed due to the force of the swelling. **Figure 5.**

This dis-organized tissue is not as strong as the original tissue it is replacing and may be the cause of many re-injuries as the horse goes back to work.

In the presence of an organizing force, such as a stretch or pull, the collagen and elastin fibers will align with that force and be organized along that line of strain provided by the force. For example, this force or stretch could be the tension coming from the reticular fibers bridging a laceration and pulling it closed which will direct the fibroblasts to lay down collagen along the line of strain provided by

Too often when our horses are injured we follow the advice of "Bute and rest". Unfortunately the lack of work implied in "rest" does not provide and organizing force for the repairing tissue. This can result in a random alignment of the collagen and elastin that is weaker than the original structure. Once the horse goes back to work the weaker part can breakdown with a resulting re-injury.

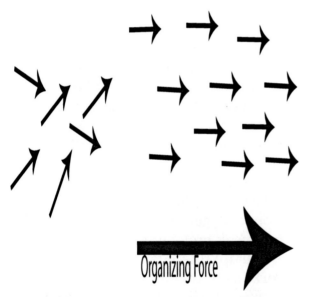

Figure 5 *Without an organizing force Collagen and Elastin will be laid down in a random fashion. The organizing force "tells" the fibroblasts how to orient the fibers they are laying down to have the maximum strength. The organizing force can come from a random postural pattern, i.e. a limp which is not desirable, or from a Myofascial Release stroke.*

the reticular fibers. However, this may not be the optimum alignment for the tissue and may result in a weak and dis-organized area in the fascia. This weak area will have a tendency to re-injury.

The application of an organizing stretch has to be performed before the collagen interfiber cross links become too strong and resist any re-organization. After this time, for instance in the case of a scar, these cross links would have to be broken and the new collagen organized with a stretch to provide an optimal tissue organization.

In the case of a stress or strain that is long lasting, for instance a postural issue or a chronic shoeing problem, the collagen and elastin fibers will line up along the line of the strain to reinforce the fascial web and become thicker in those areas. (Remember that the body is constantly laying down new tissue and will react to the forces that are present at the time the new tissue is being laid down.)

This tissue buildup can restrict movement in those areas. Similar to driving a car in a rut, movement will be easier along these strain lines. Unfortunately, if this restricted movement pattern lasts long, it will be ingrained into the horse's nervous system as the body seeks a movement *homeostasis* by following the path of least resistance. (By homeostasis here we mean the body's inherent ability to operate with energy efficiency.)

This is often the cause of a horse

A common example of this occurs in the horse's girth area. The strain provided by the girth—an outside influence pulling on the fascia—will cause the body to lay down more tissue to support the movement there. Unfortunately asking the horse to bend somewhere other than around this tissue can result in problems that are misinterpreted as an "attitude" problem rather than a physical limitation.

This can lead to a cinchy horse, as well as a serratus ventralis shortening and restriction of the scapula.

seemingly not being able to learn new movements. Their body does not experience the new movement as efficient and therefore doesn't change its current movement pattern to adapt. (Ask yourself if it is smarter to retain an apparently efficient movement pattern or change to one that is less efficient?)

Fascial release work can remove

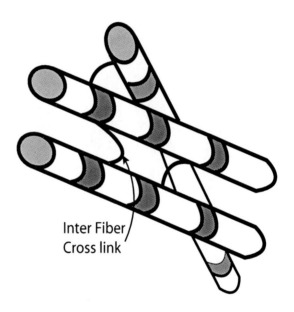

Inter Fiber / Cross link

Figure 6 *If the collagen fibers come too close together, such as in dehydrated tissue, they will develop hydrostatic cross-links between them.*

these restrictions, giving the horse and rider a fresh body to build on.

Lack of movement in the fascial web, which could occur for example with poorly fitted equipment, can cause a reduction in tissue hydration. This lack of hydration, especially within the ground substance, allows the collagen fibers to come closer together and form *hydrostatic* bonds with each other. **Figure 6**

This bond, similar to a snag in a T-shirt, reduces the fascia's ability to expand to accommodate

An excellent example of a hydrostatic bond, or crosslink, occurs when one takes plastic wrap off the roll. The stored energy of being rolled up causes the plastic wrap to re-roll and cling to itself. This is a weak, easily broken, hydrostatic bond. Hydrostatic bonds are the attraction of H2O (water) molecules to each other. These bonds are initially weak, but become stronger over time. If you allowed the plastic wrap to sit in a -re-rolled up state it would be harder to straighten it out.

This is the same occurrence with the hydrostatic bonds initially made in wound healing. They are initially weak and easily broken—therefore we must be careful not to disrupt them—and become much stronger over time.

Contrast the plastic wrap with Aluminum foil which exhibits more a molecular bond that happens at the intercellular level.

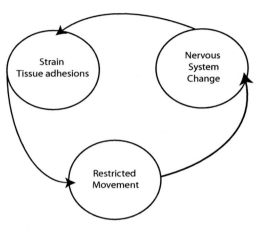

Figure 7 *Soft tissue strain, if not removed, will eventually result in a restricted pattern of movement which will become a part of the nervous system's movement pattern memory.*

movement. This can also lead to further strain patterns as the fascia's movement is reduced, thus setting up a cycle of strain and adaptation. All of these can lead to a movement pattern that is accommodating this strain and not as efficient. **Figure 7**

This accommodation of the strain can lead to problems in the joints, for example, especially if the soft tissue pulls on the joint are not balanced. This lack of soft tissue balance around the joint can cause a rotation and shortening. This can lead to one portion of the joint surface being worn more quickly from receiving

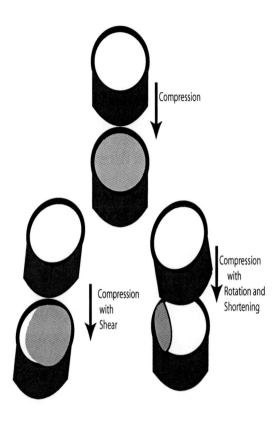

Compression

Compression
with
Shear

Compression
with
Rotation and
Shortening

Figure 8 *The effects of imbalance can be seen in this illustration the gray area represents the amount of joint surface that is bearing weight.*

more compression forces. (This is one explanation of how a joint becomes arthritic. The soft tissue imbalances around the joint cause a rotation and a reduction in the joint space. Rotations in a joint are almost always accompanied by a shortening in the joint space.) **Figure 8** This shortened space corresponds with the side that is bearing more of the compressive

forces on the joint. The cartilage on this side wears down quicker than the other surfaces. This worn down cartilage is then replaced with bone as the body tries to repair itself. (The avascular nature of cartilage makes it difficult for it to repair itself. The cartilage depends on movement, compression to bring in nutrition and to remove cellular waste products.)

These strain patterns can be cumulative, building on each other over time. With this strain pattern accumulation can come a time where the horse's body breaks down and we erroneously believe that it was an acute incident rather than a long term buildup of small insults. This is what is commonly known as *layering*.

Layering of patterns can also result in our chasing after physical symptoms as one layer is removed and reveals the symptom of another layer.

Keep this layering concept in mind as you work on symptoms.

If you find that you've relieved one symptom and another has replaced it, you may need to step back and reevaluate your strategy, and incorporate more balancing of the tissue, which is a more wholistic way of working with the fascia.

Parts versus the Whole

While our conventional understanding of anatomy is the anatomy of parts, the understanding of the anatomy of fascia has to be of the whole. Conventional anatomy assumes that the body is made up of parts, when in reality, no parts exist by themselves in the body. It is useful and expedient for understanding anatomy to separate the body into parts; however, to actually find these parts one would have to separate them from the whole, using some instrument like a scalpel, a laser, etc.

We understand from the study of embryologically, that all of the trillions of cells that make up an equine body came from one fertilized ovum. From this one egg and sperm combination all of the specialized cells in the body, came into being. From the time the sperm fertilized the egg, there was never a separation of body parts.

While there are no actual separate body parts in the body, in this book we will still talk about them as if there were, using such terms as *superficial, deep* or *myofascia* as well as *muscles, tendons, ligaments, front* and *rear end.* We trust that as you read and as you work, you can hold on to the reality of the body being an integrated whole.

Muscle Organization

Fascia, organizes the muscle into its basic functional units.

Each of these functional units: myofibril, fiber and bundle up to the muscle is encased and defined by fascia. The smallest organizational unit in a muscle is the *fiber.* Similar to the organization of collagen the muscle

> When we consider that water makes up to 70% of the extra cellular matrix, it becomes apparent that the hydration of the fascia is an important consideration.
>
> If we used a sponge as an analogy for fascia, the effects on the water in the fascia by various movements, stretching, compression and twisting could be readily seen by manipulating the sponge.
>
> Stretching a sponge has little effect on the water, while compression and twisting has a great effect. A simple conclusion can be drawn from this: if you want to move the water in fascia, it is best to compress it or put a twist into it.

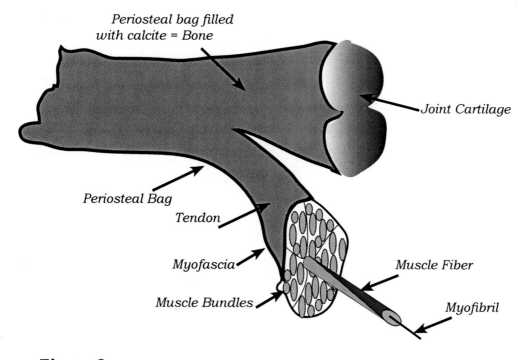

Periosteal bag filled with calcite = Bone

Joint Cartilage

Periosteal Bag

Tendon

Myofascia

Muscle Fiber

Muscle Bundles

Myofibril

Figure 9 *The only way to separate fascia from muscle, muscle from tendon or tendon from bone is to cut it. The difference in these is only in their collagen and elastin makeup. This figure deliberately shows these "elements" as being unified in an attempt to break the impression we have from anatomy books that they are parts.*

The fascial "bags", endomysium, perimysium, etc. are filled with calcites to form the bone and give it both flexibility and strength.

fiber's muscle cells are linked in a line to each other.

The muscle fibers aggregate into *myofibrils* surrounded and defined by a fascial casing, the *endomysium.*

The myofibrils bundle together into a *fascicle* which is held together by the facia *perimysium.*

Finally the fascicles are bundled and surrounded by the fascia *epimysium* which is the outermost muscle fascial sheath, commonly

called the *myofascia* (myo = muscle). (The epimysium is what we are working with in myofascial release.) **Figure 9**

The outermost layer of epimysium (myofascia) gives the muscle its distinction and separation from the other muscles of the body. It is also the epimysium that becomes the periosteum of the bone while the other embryonic facial layers form the tubules in the bone where mineral calcites are laid down to give the bone its strength. When one looks at an old skeleton—one in a museum for instance—what one is seeing is the remaining calcites not the living bone. Cutting one of these old bones open one will see the pattern of tubules that were originally defined by fascia.

While these layers of tissue—periosteum, tendon, ligament and muscle—exist in a spatial sense, their only true distinction from each other is in their collagen and elastin content. More collagen results in more rigidity and will be found in the tissue that needs this: the periosteal bag of bone, ligaments and tendons... More elastin results in more elasticity, as found in: myofascia, the surrounding of the organs...

The detailed distinction that we see in the anatomy books—bones are clean and separate from tendons, which are separate from muscles—between these structures are artistic renditions and convenient labels. This separation is the result of a sharp instrument dissecting these structures out of their natural relationship to each other. **Figure 9**

Nerves, veins and arteries all travel through the fascia. If there is an adhesion to their path they can be negatively affected. When we release these adhesions it is not uncommon to see more blood flow, i.e. the veins are visible.

All of these structures have to be able to expand and contract with movement. For example; the Sciatic Nerve has to expand approximately 1.5 to 2.0 inches in a human bending over to touch their toes. It also has to return to its original length when the person stands up.

Adhesions in the preventing this motion will contribute to the horse's movement not being as balanced as possible.

Fascial Adhesions

Collagen and elastin, are continually being laid down by the fibroblasts[11] and organizing along the mechanical lines of strain in the fascia. As mentioned before, the more powerful and sustained the force of the strain, the thicker the fascia (collagen, elastin and ground substance) will be in that area to compensate for the strain.

One common adhesion, that we are all familiar with, is scar

tissue. Scar tissue is collagen and elastin—fascia—that is deposited in areas of lacerative injury. The injury heals through the action of the reticular fibers pulling the edges of the laceration together and forming an framework for the collagen, elastin and ground substance. Unfortunately, if there is an absence of an *organizing* force on the scar fascia—to align the collagen and elastin—the scar will become a random array of collagen and elastin, with little mobility.[12] If the original laceration was extensive, this lack of organization in the scar can cause a disruption in the fascia's ability to move smoothly. (This is a common issue with the castration scars of geldings. If not released they can cause a movement problem with the rear legs.)

Similarly, when there is little movement between muscle groups, such as in a lay up for injury recovery—remember the "bute and rest" discussion—the fascial sheaths can form *hydrostatic bonds*. These are bonds are known as *adhesions*. Adhesions between the myofascial sheaths surrounding muscles can cause them to lose their independent movement. These myofascial adhesions—between adjoining muscles—can cause the muscle to drag its neighboring muscle's fascial sheath with every contraction or extension. This not only creates a very inefficient movement but can set up the muscle imbalances and torsions discussed earlier. (**Adaptation to Injury and Insult section.**)

Because fascia and muscle are responsible for moving the *bag* in which the bones are contained, restricted fascia could pull a horse's bones out of proper joint alignment, causing dysfunctional movement patterns which could result in increased joint wear.

Adhesions (initially weak hydrostatic cross links) can also develop within the fascial sheaths themselves when collagen fibers become intertwined and attract each other.[13] This can happen because of a reduction in the *hydration* of the tissue. You can imagine what this feels like if you've ever put on some clothes that were a little too tight and restrict your movement. A comedic example of this can be seen in the movie *Men in Black,* where one of the characters, from another planet, inhabits the skin of a human. Unfortunately for him, this "body suit" doesn't fit very well. The actor does a great job of showing the effects of shortened fascia on movement.

Fascial release works to remove these intra and inter-muscular adhesions, thereby allowing the body to move more efficiently.

Range of Motion

Range of Motion (ROM)—*is defined as the movement range that a body part, usually a joint, can move through before coming to a barrier. It is further delineated as:*

Passive ROM—*is the ROM that another, person in this case, can take the part through while the horse is not resisting the movement. For example taking the shoulder forward and backward to the natural stopping point.*

Passive ROM is hard to judge with another being that doesn't communicate verbally with us—we have to be able to tell the other not to resist our movement of their body part. It is even hard to judge it with other humans that may unintentionally resist us.

Basically we take the leg, for instance, and move it—protract or retract—until we reach a barrier or restriction to the movement. This Range is the Passive ROM, which is the maximum available motion in that particular joint, muscle or fascial system.

Active ROM—*is the ROM that the horse has access to actively in normal movement. The horse will move the body part until it meets a barrier and not proceed further. It is this program of meeting a barrier that causes the resistance to the movement beyond this point, encountered in the passive ROM test.*

Usually the motion of Passive ROM is greater than that of Active ROM. Active ROM is limited by the barriers or restrictions that are incorporated into the nervous system's movement map. Passive ROM does not require the use of the subject's nervous system.

Increasing Active ROM is a benefit of MFR.

Just as importantly, removing these adhesions allows the joints to move in their intended plane of motion, without rotations caused by restricted soft tissue.

Myofascial release can also remove pressure put on nerves, veins and arteries that is created by fascial adhesions within the fascial pathways that these vital structures occupy.

Conclusions and Review

Fascia is a densely woven web of connective tissue made up of collagen and elastin fibers suspended in a ground substance of water and GAGs. It provides the form and covering of every muscle, bone, nerve, artery and vein as well as all of our internal organs: heart, lungs, brain, spinal cord, the lot of them.

The fascial network is the one structure in the body that exists from head to foot without interruption. In the normal healthy and hydrated state, fascia has the ability to stretch and move without restriction. Through physical trauma, poor posture, lack of movement or inflammation, the fascia can lose its pliability.

With lack of motion it becomes dehydrated, tight, restricted and a source of tension and restricted Range of Motion (ROM) and may develop adhesions between adjacent fascial planes or sheaths.

Fascial release is different than normal stretching in that it engages the adhesions in the fascia and removes them. This is accomplished by applying a sustained pressure to the fascia and waiting for the ground substance to change from a gel to a sol. Because of the ubiquitous nature of fascia, restrictions in one part of the body may cause problems a great distance from that site.

Exercises and More Study

Try this exercise to see how your fascial pattern works. Cross your arms over your chest. Now, cross your arms the other way. Do you feel more restricted and less comfortable? The first way represents your habitual pattern, the way that feels easier to your nervous system. This is called your "tissue homeostasis". Can you see how this pattern was automatic and ingrained in the nervous system? This ingrained automatic response is true of our entire voluntary movement repertoire, it will follow the path of least resistance as we try to achieve homeostasis.

Get an orange or grapefruit. Take a look at the skin and see how it is organized. Try to feel through the skin to the next layer. Then try to feel through the skin to the pulpy part.

Using a knife to cut the fruit in half notice how the skin is actually adhered to the inside portion by a thick tissue. This is the fruit's superficial fascia. See how the slices inside are separated by a tissue of a slightly different consistency, i.e. collagen and elastin makeup? This is similar to the way myofascia functions in separating the muscles. (In a mammal this separation between the muscles, is called a *muscle septum*.) The fruit is further organized into separate cells, these are representative of the muscle fibers. Can you see the pockets and pouches that were described in this chapter, in this fruit? Can you also see that the type of instrument you use to separate the parts of the whole fruit determines how many parts you think there are? This is how our understanding of anatomy evolved.

As we humans developed more precise tools, to cut into the body in smaller pieces, we came up with names for these smaller pieces. Somewhere along the way of developing our tools of dissection we forgot that what we were doing was cutting into a whole body and not separating something that was once parts. (Some people suggest that before the Industrial Revolution the body was still viewed as a whole. After the advent of machines we started to see it as parts that made up a whole, with the repair of the parts being possible.)

Endnotes

1. Chiquat M, Renado AS, Huber F, Fluck M. "How do fibroblasts translate mechanical signals into changes in ECM production?". Bern: Elesevier. Matrix Biology 2003; 22(1):73-80.

2. You can see, with this inter-connectedness, where a postural issue can have an effect on other areas of the body.

3. Myers T. Anatomy Trains. Edinburgh: Churchill Livingstone; 2001.

4. In the next Volume, Equine Structural Integration, we'll go over this in detail. Now we can assume that deviations seen in movement are equivalent to fascial holding patterns.

5. Remember, there are fibroblasts and chondrocytes in the matrix. The ground substance is what these swim in.

6. We see this gel/sol relationship in Jell-O. When it is heated it is a solution when it is cool it is a solid.

7. Oschman, J. Readings in the Scientific Basis of Bodywork. Dover, NH: NORA; 1997.

8. Travell J, Simmons D, Myofascial

pain and dysfunction: The Trigger Point Manual. vol. 1. Baltimore: Williams and Wilkins; 1983.

9. A phase change is the name of the event where a substance changes from a solid to a liquid or gas or vice versa. For instance, water, at sea level, changes phase from a liquid to a solid, ice, at 32 degrees Fahrenheit and to a gas, steam, at 212 degrees Fahrenheit.

10. The collagen molecules will form what are called *cross links* at the molecular level to provide strength to the molecules. Unfortunately the term cross links is also used in the therapy books to describe the dysfunctional hydrostatic bond that occurs between fascial units. We'll differentiate the hydrostatic bonds from cross links by labelling them as adhesions.

11. Blast cells are those that lay a material down. For instance, *osteo*blasts lay down bone. Clast cells are responsible for removing the material the blast cell laid down—when it is no longer needed. (An example would be a bone spur. The tensional strain on a the periosteum, from a chronically contracted or misaligned muscle, can result in blast cells laying down bone to balance the strain. If through fascial release or some other balancing modality the strain is removed, clast cells will move in and remove the calcite, thereby reducing the spur.) These are the same cells, blast or clast, only doing a different job.

12. Because of the random arrangement of collagen and elastin of most scars they are not as strong as the original fascia. This is one of the reasons why a bowed tendon that is healed with the prescription of stall rest will not be as strong as the original tendon and may re-bow after work

is introduced again.
13. Again the distinction, caused by the anatomy of parts, is that the collagen fibers of one fascial sheath are hydrostatically bonded with those of another fascial sheath or layer.

Contents

The Horse

Nature and Nurture

The Nature of Horses

All animals possess the ability to be prey and predator. If we were to chart these characteristics from predator to prey; the *domestic* horse would fall as far to the prey end of this continuum as possible.

This is both a product of the inherent nature of horses as grazing animals and the domestication of the horse by humans. These two forces *nature and nurture* worked together to create a relatively docile animal that we work with today.

The only horses that primitive humans could begin to domesticate were the ones that could be easily caught; easily is a relative term as it is used here. The horses that could not be caught were probably hunted and eaten.

Once the horses were caught and put into a breeding program, the more aggressive animals would have been culled from the herd as too dangerous to work with. This left the more docile horses to breed and pass on their genes, thereby *selecting* for animals easier to work with. So, even that *wild animal* you are confronting at the local dressage barn is tamer than the ones our ancestors met.

If we take this genetic argument one step further to what we currently call *wild horses* here in the West; we can conclude that only *domesticated* horses— that were re-introduced by the Europeans to the Americas— escaped to re-populate the plains of North America. Our *wild* mustangs have had 500 years of being wild while their ancestors were domesticated for a couple of thousand years. The equine gene pool has the influence of humans permeating it, no matter whether the horse is wild or domestic.

The fact that domestic horses— which escaped from human control—have survived to become the "wild" horses of North America, leads us to the conclusion that the horse retains the nervous system *program*, if you will, to become self sufficient given the proper environment—without the care of humans.

In addition, this program is always somewhere beneath the surface of our domestic horse ready to express itself. (We encounter this program as a flight or fight response as well as a natural creation of a band or herd when horses are together.) Part of this program includes an affinity towards humans that allowed the horse to be domesticated to begin with. This is good news for us!

The Nurture of Horses

The plains and steppes are wide open spaces, gently undulating with few trees or obstacles to run into or jump over. The horse, in its evolution did not need to turn quickly to avoid trees, or jump when running from predators. It required speed rather than agility to escape.

With human intervention and domestication we've been able to select horses with more agility than their naturally evolved counterpart would have had. (The Mustangs are not under the same selective breeding program as domestic horses; they must survive in an open environment which makes them an excellent choice for sports that require endurance.)

Having evolved primarily on the plains, two elements are prominent in the horse's survival makeup: awareness of and running from predators. I'll call them *Sight* and *Flight*. The horse evolved by being able to see the predator and run away from it. Remove either of these two primary, primal defenses and you'll create a potential problem for the horse and for yourself.

The horse evolved sharing the burden of being watchful of predators with other horses in a herd. (Without the herd to share

Have you ever noticed, in your pasture, that there is always one horse on alert, while the others may be sleeping. At no time does the entire herd take a nap together.

security with a horse would be easy prey when it went to sleep.)

This herd, band or community has always been essential to the horse's survival; with each individual contributing both to that survival and sharing in raising the young. (The raising of the young is something our domestic horse keeping lacks.)

In a *natural* horse herd there are members of both sexes, but no neutered or spayed animals. These two key elements: having members of both sexes and living with the herd, are often lost in how we keep horses today. First, stallions are removed from the herd to avoid *accidental* breeding. (Neutered animals are not a *natural* part of a wild herd.) Second, horses are often separated in barns where they can't see each other; this is not only unnatural but it puts an undue stress on the animals. (Have you ever noticed that horses are noisiest when they can't see each other? Contrast this to how little noise there is in a pasture while a herd is out grazing.)

The *leader* of the herd is the dominant female; while

the *protector* of the herd is the dominant male. In this case dominance doesn't mean most *aggressive* it means most *aware* of the surroundings and the possible

> *Not only is awareness a requirement in the stallion as herd protector, this must be coupled with an ability to discriminate threat from non-threat. If the stallion causes the herd to move away from imagined threats the herd looses valuable grazing time.*

threats to the herd.

In the open prairie environment the individual horse is almost always in visual contact with the herd, reducing to a minimum the need for vocalization. In fact, horses only *call* to each other when there is some stress in their life—as when someone they can not see enters their barn.

Body Language

Horses usually avoid making a loud noise that can attract predators but they do vocalize in a close manner, a mother nickering to her foal for instance or snorting at a horse or human that is in their space. However, the primary means of communication between horses is visual—*body language.* (Other signals imperceptible to a human's awareness that we perhaps take as telepathic are also involved .)

The body language of the horse is incredibly complex, the swish of a tail in irritation, the licking of lips in submission, the blinking of eyes, the licking of another horse or human to show dominance over them, the curl of a neck... Understanding this body language separates the horseman from the hobbyist. Failure to understand this language can lead the human and horse into a potential conflict.

Take for instance the *pinning of ears*, which precedes the baring of teeth or occasionally a kick. This pinning is the last sentence in a long paragraph of communication before the fight or frustration—I want to replace fight with frustration as the motivation for their action—response takes place. Its purpose is not to indicate *attack* aggression, although with frustration at not being heard aggression may follow; rather it is an expression of *defensive* aggression, and serves to protect the sensitive *Atlanto Occipital* joint. It is much better to lose a little ear than to have the spinal cord severed from a bite at the AO. (If you watch a wild rabbit and you'll see the same pinning of the ears both before and while they run away. Maybe the rabbit is bluffing at being a mean animal to scare predators away.)

The problem between horses and people occurs when we do not see the entire body language sequence that leads up to something like pinned ears. This failure can lead the human to label a frustrated horse as aggressive and something to be feared rather than understood. This fear, can inadvertently alter the *herd* dynamic placing the horse higher in the herd hierarchy than the human. The labeling of the horse as aggressive can also prevent the human from understanding and correcting the behavior, that evoked the horse's frustration.

Given that the horse evolved in a visually open environment, the primary tool for assessing danger is the eye. The ears and nose are used as secondary senses to the eye. The horse's eye sits on top of a long neck that allows it to be positioned to see predators.

When the other horses in the herd sense the body language of fear—whether from another horse or a human—they are primed to react. The reaction can be anything from running away to trying to get a better idea of what caused the fear in the other.

To sense the threat the horses will raise their heads and bring their hearing and smell, as well as sight, to bear on the threat.

Within the herd it is imperative that the horses respond to the survival directives of the stallion in charge of security. Not to respond could lead to being caught by a predator. As mentioned earlier, it is important that the stallion does not also give out false alarms.

Many horse/human interaction problems stem from the human's body language giving the horse a mixed message. Here is an example: A person goes into the pasture, catches their horse and leads it from the herd. When one of the herd comes up to investigate, the person becomes tense, telling the horses—through body language—that there's something to be afraid of. The horses raise their heads to see, hear and smell the threat. The horses don't think it is them that the person fears, so there must be something else. Now the two horses look for the threat and the person becomes more fearful and then harshly and aggressively corrects the horse for acting like a horse; raising their head. This misreading of the horse's natural way of being and then punishing it for doing what comes naturally, can cause a distrust of the person in the horse. Unfortunately I see this a lot with people who are afraid of their horses, or just aren't aware of the environment, the herd and how the horse will naturally react.

Eyes and Vision

The horse has a 350 degree *field of vision*, with the 10 degrees that it is directly to the rear being a blind spot. Each eye has about a 160 degree field of vision. This is the totality of their front and *peripheral vision.* Most of this visual range is able to see movement but not specific details. A prey animal needs only to see the movement of a predator within a large field of vision to react to it. A small shift in the horses head position brings the object into better focus and therefore allows it to be identified as a friend or foe.

More specifically the horse sees movement that is not expected. In fact, this is a hard-wired reptilian brain function in all mammals. We all react more to visual movement than we do to static events.

The *visual acuity* of a horse looking straight ahead at an object at 20 feet is about as good as a person looking at the same object at 33 feet. From this we can postulate that a horse has 60% of the visual acuity of a human. The horse has 1.5 times the visual acuity of a dog and 3 times that of a cat. This is a good arrangement for a prey animal that allows it to

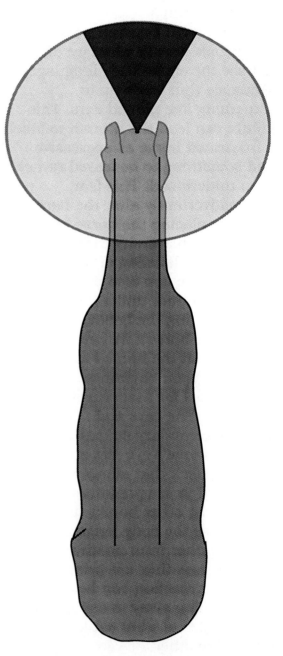

Figure 1 *The horse has a field of vision of approximately 350 degrees, with a blind spot directly behind it.*

see predators before they see it!

Horse vision is dichromatic; they see in two colors. They have the cones required to see in three colors within their eyes but these are not utilized; an interesting evolutionary factoid.

The horse's field of vision is monocular within most of the range, and binocular in the 60-70 degree area directly in front of it. (The black area in Fig. 1) The 10 degrees that the horse cannot see is directly behind its head—the place where the lion attacks and where riders also sit! This is the reason why one never wants to startle a horse from behind; it can't see you and may give you a quick kick before running away. The horse has another *blind spot* under the head; like us it can't see under its chin.

The horse experiences its world through this tremendous peripheral vision and expects that you experience it the same way. The result is that horses may be signaling to us their irritation but we can't see it; this could result in a frustrated horse and our being bitten or kicked!

There's an old horseman's myth that horses only recognize what they see with the eye that is seeing it. The myth is that a horse seeing

Humans are predators to the horse. One easy way to tell a predator is by the location of the eyes. Predators have eyes in the front of their face.

Looking a horse in the eyes or face with your intense stare, or **predator eyes**, *will cause the animal to be much more nervous around you.*

a spooky object on the right side, will spook at the same object when they see on the left side because they don't recognize it as something they've already seen. This is a myth and has been proven wrong by many researchers.

Humans only have approximately 180 degrees of field of vision, if we're lucky. Unfortunately the horse doesn't know this and may be talking to us with a part of its body that is out of our visual field. This can lead to a communication problem and frustration on the horse's part. If you are working

It is the prey animal with a movement aberration that gets the most attention from the predator - remember the reptilian brain seeing movement first. Prey that has a locomotor problem is easier to catch and increases the energy gained from the energy investment required to catch it.

on a horse and you sense that it is acting frustrated you may want to take the possibility that you haven't seen its signals into consideration!

If you have an opportunity to watch a horse moving freely, in an arena or round pen, turn your predator attention on and see if the horse's body changes.

Walk into a pasture of horses that know you. Walk towards a grazing horse looking at the sky and see how close you get before they react to you. Then try it with your predator eyes on and see how far, not close, you get!

Therapist or Tiger

It is important to recognize that the horse's body language will cue you to the times when you, the horse or the owner/handler move up or down in the herd hierarchy. It is the difference between being safe or not. Just as important for the therapist, is the recognition that the therapeutic environment/ relationship is changing with these changes in this three animal herd hierarchy—you the horse and the handler make up the herd.

We need to be aware of these possible changes to make the proper intervention to the horse's body.

Bringing your *tiger claws* out to work with a scar is fine as long as the horse respects you as a protector. It is very dangerous if the horse sees you as lower in the pecking order or worse as a predator! If you are seen as lower in the herd hierarchy you may get an attitude-adjusting bite as you insult a horse that sees itself higher in the herd. If you are seen as a predator you may evoke a fight response, especially if the horse can't escape you. Putting your predator eyes on a horse could also provoke a flight/fight response from the horse.

Besides the potential for the horse to want to escape or fight you, there's another reason why we don't want to show a predator attitude when we are working with horses. Humans *hunt* other animals and we *eat* horses. Evolutionarily we are predators, and the horse will act as though it is in the presence of a predator rather than a therapist.

In the presence of a predator the prey animal's nervous system will not be available to us to make a therapeutic intervention. It will try to mask any locomotor problems it has from us, so we don't see it as an easy kill.

I experienced this in my Rolfing® training where we were required to stand in front of the class in our underwear while the other students tried to *read* our body's structural patterns for the teachers. Those of us in the front of the *predators,* whose predator eyes were looking for structural flaws in our body, shifted nervously in front of them. Revealing our *flaws* is not a comfortable thing to do, even in a safe classroom.

More Domestication

In domestication the horses are taken away from their mothers when they can be weaned, so the mare can be bred again. This practice of weaning is prevalent even if the mare is not to be re-bred. This takes the young horse away from the learning environment of the herd and puts it in with other youngsters until it is old enough to be physically secure with the older horses.

This is a body growth measure of maturity not a mental one. What we encounter when we work with most domestic horses are ones that are immature in their horseyness and often not very well mannered. Couple this stunted mental maturity with an owner that is not that *horsey* and you've got a recipe for trouble. Most domestic horses are confused about what they are, horse or human, and even more dangerously they are confused about what the humans are!

It is important for your own safety that you spend some time with your new clients watching how they and their horses interact. See if the horse and owner respect each other and evaluate what kind of environment/herd you are entering. If they don't respect each other then you'll need to make sure you stay aware of both of them while you are working.

You want to know that the handler is aware of where you and the horse are. That they won't inadvertently do something to irritate the horse or move the horse into you.

Remember, awareness will put you at the top of the herd hierarchy in the horse's mind, and this is where you want to be since the human member of the herd usually doesn't weigh over a 1000 lbs. or kick.

Chapter Contents

Equine Structure and Movement

Equine Structure

The Foot

The horse's foot evolved from three toes (with 3 phalanges making up each toe) to one toe (with 3 phalanges). The second and fourth metacarpal-tarsal bones are still present as the *splint bones* and can be palpated on the side of the third metacarpal-tarsal bone or *Canon Bone.*

The horse's hoof is akin to our finger nail and is continually growing—as a rule of thumb a completely new hoof takes about a year to grow—to compensate for the wear it experiences as the horse moves over abrasive surfaces. With man's usage of the horse for more than its typical walk to forage and occasionally flight from a predator, the hoof wears faster than it grows, so the horseshoe was invented to compensate for this increased wear. Originally the shoe was held on by strings, the *Hippo Sandal*; later, as the technique was developed, the strings were replaced with nails.

The wall—the outside of the horses hoof—will grow at a rate that accommodates the pressure put on that wall by the structures above it. **Figure 1.** In other words, if the horse's weight is distributed

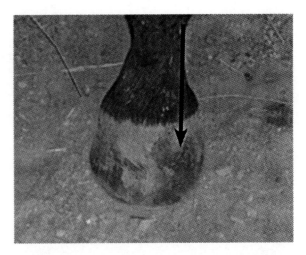

Figure 1. *Hoof Stresses. The weight of the body is transferring down the line of the arrow, the horse will grow more foot on that side to compensate for the increased wear of the hoof wall on that side. If the foot is shod, the nails on this side will show more wear. The nail wear on the shod foot is indicative of the weight transfer through the foot.*

to the outside of the hoof, rather than down the center, then the outside wall will grow faster than the inside wall to compensate for the increased wear on the outside of the hoof.

The weight transfer through the foot will also affect its overall size, the smaller foot will be the one that consistently carries less weight. This *weight shift* can be associated with a preference for the side that carries more weight— because of some structural issue or habit—or may be attributed to *handedness*, similar to a human preference for using the left or right hand. For instance, horses with a chronically sore foot will raise up off of that foot to relieve the pain. This can result in a contracted shoulder on that side. (The fascia in the shoulder and leg will become tighter to help the muscles maintain the contraction

Figure 2. *Horseshoe wear can tell us a lot about the structures above. The nails will have more wear on the side that bears most of the weight (circle). The toe will show how the foot breaks over in protraction.*

In the shoe shown the Farrier has "rolled" the toes to promote faster break over to make it easier for the front foot to move out of the way of the rear feet (black arrow). This is a common tactic for horses that step on and pull front shoes with their rear feet.

. You should make note of this when you first work with the horse as it influences the foot timing and flight.

in a more energy efficient way.) It may also result in a horse's resistance to putting weight on the sore foot. The may notice this when they clean out the foot on the other side, which requires the sore foot to bear more weight. You may be told something like, "he has a sore shoulder and won't stand for me to pick out his foot". Usually these problems will be noted by the farrier before you are called to work with the horse.

Letting out a shoulder on a horse with a sore foot will be removing the positive compensation for the soreness and may result in a less than positive reaction by the horse. If the foot is still sore, the horse may look lame after you release the shoulder. The problem, the sore foot, hasn't been relieved, and needs to be before the horse will be comfortable weighting it correctly. This is veterinary or farrier issue.

Given all this, when you encounter a horse with shoes, **Figure 2**, you can tell quite a lot about how they transfer weight through their leg by looking at the wear pattern of the nail heads on the bottom of the shoe. Ask yourself these questions: Are the nails worn more on one side or the other? Is the shoe worn in the front center or off to one side? Is the foot balanced?

The Front Suspension

The shoulders and front legs of the horse are not attached to the rest of the body through a bone—the human *clavicle* attaches our *shoulder girdle* to our *axial skeleton*—since the horse does not have a clavicle. This allows for a separation of the movement of the *front appendicular skeleton* (the legs are the appendicular skeleton) from the the *axial skeleton* (the rest of the body), similar to an off road vehicle's independent suspension system. As shown in **Figure 3**.

The *axial skeleton* (the body) of the horse is suspended from the scapulae and legs (humerus, radius, and etc.) by the pectoral and the serratus ventralis muscles. These three soft tissue structures are known as the *Thoracic Sling*. (I'm making a distinction here between the body and the neck. There are soft tissue structures

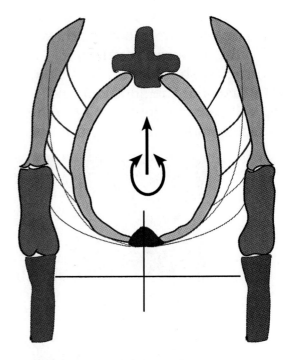

Figure 3. *The front of the horse has no boney connection to the rest of the body.*

The sternum should be equidistant from each humerus. (The pectorals are depicted in Figure 3 as thin lines while the serratus is the thicker lines.) Rotations in the body/spine will cause the sternum to be off center between the legs.

> *To check for a thoracic rotation I just close my eyes and run my hand down the sternum, if it feels like it is going off to one side there's a rotation. Often there is a compensatory rotation, as well as the soft tissue bracing that is caused by someone mounting the horse from the ground.*

that attach the neck to the front limbs that aren't mentioned here.) This allows the body to rotate and elevate without disturbing the front legs. It also allows—within limits— the legs to move without disturbing the body.

As you can see, from **Figure 3,** any *contraction holding pattern* in the pectorals or serrati can show up as a rotation in the body or as a

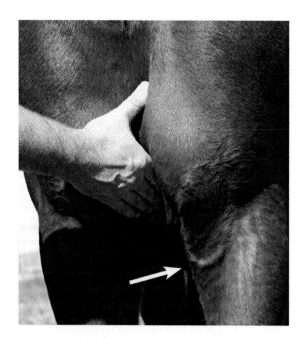

Figure 4 *Checking the relative position of the sternum to determine if there is a twist in the thorax. The hand follows the arrow's path. The sternum should go straight back, not feel like there is a twist or movement to one side.*

restriction in the shoulder.

This body rotation can be reflected through the spine affecting the rear of the horse. But more often the horse will develop a compensatory strategy in the contra-lateral front limb. Either raising that limb or leaning on it. The presence of a *body rotation* can be determined by the relative position of the sternum to the humerus as measured from side to side.

You can also predict, from **Figure 3,** that in order for the body to rise between the legs, the scapula will have to move laterally to provide a mechanical advantage to the thoracic sling muscles. Without this lateral movement the angle of pull of these muscles will bring the front limbs into the body removing the advantage of having an independent front end. Unfortunately, this lateral movement of the shoulders can be restricted by saddles that don't fit properly are not positioned correctly or by riders off balance. This restriction leads to a *girthy/cinchy* horse.

The front legs hang from the body and neck by the brachiocephalicus, rhomboids, lattisimus dorsi, cervical serratus and trapezius.

Here we have a concept that may be foreign to you. A body suspended from the legs and the legs suspended from the body. This is a very common Structural Integration way of describing the body.

If the front of the horse is the steering mechanism, the rear of the horse can be thought of as the engine or drive train. It is from the rear that the horse pushes the body forward with a minimum amount of *pulling* from the front that occurs from friction on the front feet during their

Figure 5. *Mechanical Energy Flow moving from the rear legs through the spine to the head and out the forehead. Like the movement of a pendulum the rear legs create a wave of energy through the spine and soft tissue of the body.*

Figure 6 *Reflected Energy Flow. The energy from the rear is restricted by the shoulders or rider, with some portion of the wave reflected back towards the rear. This sets up "standing waves" of energy that can often be seen in a rider's arms—as elbows flapping—as well as an uncomfortable ride.*

retraction. (Some horses pull from the front when they move; this is undesirable and an indication of tight shoulders which prevents a transfer of weight—Center of Gravity/Mass—to the rear.)

There is a continuity of soft tissue and bone—the axial skeleton—from the head to the rear feet which allows mechanical energy to move from the rear to the head. This sinusoidal wave of energy, from the rear to the head—produced by the rhythmic movement of the rear legs propelling the body forward—has to proceed without barrier in order to move through the spine and the head. Hence the old horse-person's

adage that the horse should *lead with its head*—resulting in the most efficient movement, **Figure 5**. Barriers to this movement will create *reflected waves* which can more easily be seen in the rider of the horse than in the horse itself, **Figure 6**.

This reflection of the mechanical energy is not a problem for the horse that is not being ridden, since it can easily move its body to accommodate it. It only becomes a problem when the added weight of the rider and equipment is added to the equation.

The un-ridden horse can throw its head backwards to move weight to the rear when it needs to and just as easily move the head forward to shift weight forward. These unrestricted shifts in the body position assure optimum balance. With a rider this is not possible.

Collection

Collection is the term that riders use to describe the movement of the horse's center of gravity from the front of the horse to the rear. This is accomplished through shifting of the weight (center of mass) of the horse from the front towards the rear. The horse, in general, carries up to 60% of its body weight over the front legs; add to this the weight of a rider and tack, and you can see the need to be able to shift

If you drop a pebble into a bath tub of water a wave will form moving out from where the pebble hit. When this wave of energy hits the side of the tub there will be another wave reflected back into the tub. This is the reflected wave that resulted from the energy hitting the barrier of the tub side. This wave is going to have less energy than the first wave and be out of phase by 180 degrees to the original. If you continue to rhythmically drop pebbles into the tub the resulting waves and the reflected waves will sometimes add up to create larger waves and sometimes subtract to create smaller ones.

We see this mostly in the increased movement of the rider's arms in a horse with shoulder restrictions. When looking at a ridden horse that is moving efficiently, the rider should look like a cork rhythmically bobbing on the waves of energy.

Figure 7 *The Center of Gravity (COG) has to move to the rear in a collected horse. The rider will feel this as a lift in their groin.*

the load to the rear. **Figure 7.**

Riding a horse that is not able to compensate for this added weight by changing the center of gravity is like riding a *plow* that is digging into the ground. There is little front end lightness and responsiveness to forward movement; this is called heavy *on the forehand* and is indicated by tissue buildup in the front as well as overly developed *hamstring muscles*—from pushing into the restriction. Unfortunately, many if not most horses are ridden without collection. This causes many of the front limb problems that are

Figure 8 *The COG (or Center of Mass if you like) moves to the rear through the upward movement of the thorax, which is caused by the soft tissue of the thoracic sling contracting. This movement "pulls" the pelvis forward which causes the rear of the horse to round. This rounding is often confused as collection; when it is only a part of it.*

so prevalent today.

The key to a horse being able to collect is the movement of the thorax dorsally, the up arrow in **Figure 3**. This shifts the weight of the thorax and rider towards the rear. The thorax rises through the contraction of the pectorals and

The misunderstanding of True Collection has resulted in the idea that holding the horse's head still, while at the same time having the rider push the body forward with their legs into this restricted head and neck will create collection, since the rear will round. It is similar to pushing a tube of toothpaste with the cap on. The toothpaste bulges to the back of the tube rounding it. (It is this rounding of the rear end of the horse that people confuse with collection.)

This does nothing to lighten the front of the horse by moving the Center of Gravity. Instead it causes more restriction and less freedom in the front of the horse.

Another problem occurs if the horse's scalene muscles are not strong enough to stabilize the neck against this added force. The neck will bend, creating a " ewe" neck and the soft tissue will harden in support of this— this causes an indentation in front of the shoulder—which can impinge on the brachio plexus, restricting the nerves and blood flow to the leg. Is this a part of navicular syndrome?

serratus muscles, which attach from the thorax to the humerus and scapula. As mentioned earlier, the arm and scapula have to be able to translate laterally allowing the lift to occur, by providing a mechanical angle for the muscles to act. Since the thorax is not circular but elliptical in its shape, room is provided for the thorax to rise. When the thorax rises, the sternum also rises, which brings the attachment of the rectus adominus more cephalad (cephalad is towards the head, the Latin *cephalicus*) causing the pubic bone to move more cephalad, this in turn causes the hips to rotate under and the back to round. **Figure 8**.

It is this rounding the rear end that many people confuse as collection. Rounding of the rear end can occur because of a restriction in the shoulders, while collection cannot. True collection is the upward movement of the thorax (COG and COM), with a secondary effect of a rounded back and movement of the pubic bone forward that causes the rear to round. The rider of a collected horse will feel the energy of the horse's movement in their seat/groin. It is really what makes riding collected horses so sensuous!

Horses will naturally collect to a greater or lesser degree of success as they move about their daily lives. It is not that important to the un-ridden horse to collect, beyond the transference of some portion of their body weight to free the forehand. It only becomes important when weight of the rider and tack is added, with the corresponding need for lightness in the front.

The key to being able to move the weight to the rear depends on the horse's freedom in its shoulders. The shoulders have to be free to assist the thorax rising and to actually create the space for the

The Neck Telescoping is accomplished through the use of the three scalene muscles.

The scalenes attach to the cervical vertebrae and the first few ribs. By holding the ribs still and contracting the scalenes, the neck will rise at the base and extend outward. If the cervical end of the scalene is held still, the ribs will move cephalad. This cephalad movement of the rib can cause a nerve entrapment syndrome. In humans this is known as Thoracic Outlet Syndrome and is associated with Carpal Tunnel Syndrome. In horses this may be one of the contributing factors for Navicular Syndrome.

One of the signs that this is happening is the depression of the tissue in front of the scapula.

thorax (the elliptical shape of the thorax has to be accommodated by the shoulders moving laterally).

Shoulder freedom is the foundation of most early dressage work, where the horse is asked to do shoulder in/out movements. A horse that is unable to collect cannot do upper level dressage work. But beyond this the ridden horse that cannot collect will not be able to compensate for the added weight of the rider and tack and will have to absorb this weight and its forces on its front legs; causing many more joint problems. Collection is imperative for all ridden horses to maintain front limb soundness over the long term.

Since collection happens to some degree during all movement, the action of the neck could also be included in its description. This action is known as *neck telescoping* and is caused by the contraction of the three *scalene* muscles. This gesture is commonly seen in Stallions and Mares as a part of their breeding ritual. In neck telescoping the base of the neck rises towards the head—allowing the energy to move out the forehead—the horse is *looking through the bridle.* Unfortunately, in the young horse the scalenes cannot overcome the resistance in the unschooled rider's hands and consequently they become *hyper-tonic.*

Chapter Contents

Equine Movement

Evaluating Movement

The true benefits from using Fascial Release for a horse is apparent when the horse is able to move better. Given this, you'll need to be able to see both the aberrant movement so you can develop a treatment plan, and the improved movement after your.

It takes a long time with a good mentor to be able to see equine movement well. One has to look at many horses and be diligent in studying what others have written, watching videos and generally being around horses while they are moving. As your skill with Myofascial Release increases, you'll need to be able to see the more subtle movement issues your client horses have. You'll also need to know when to refer your client horse to a Veterinarian.

I'm not going to attempt to describe a complete movement evaluation for a horse. What I want to write about is how to look at a horse standing and moving such that we can develop a strategy for a Fascial Release session with the animal. I'm only going to mention lameness so you'll know when to walk away from the horse and refer the animal and owner to a veterinarian.

Lameness

There are five *grades* of **lameness** defined by the severity of the movement aberration, as listed below:

Grade One
Difficult to observe; **not consistently apparent regardless** of circumstances (e.g., weight carrying, circling, moving on inclines, hard surface, etc.).

Grade Two
Difficult to observe at a walk or trotting straight line; **consistently apparent under certain circumstances** (e.g., carrying a rider, circling, moving on inclines, hard surface, etc.).

Grade Three
Consistently observable at a trot under all circumstances.

Grade Four
Obvious lameness, marked nodding, hitching or shortened stride.

Grade Five
Minimal weight bearing in motion and/or at rest; inability to move.

You'll have to decide for yourself if you want to work with a horse that is lame; I don't work with a horse above grade two lameness, as exhibited in a twenty meter circle, unless I'm referred to the horse by a veterinarian. I choose a grade two as my decision point because I can't consistently see a grade one lameness. Usually a grade one level of movement aberration is what caused the call to me in the first place. I don't feel that by working with a grade one lame horse that I am limiting the treatment options of the horse.

When you are evaluating a horse with a movement aberration/ lameness there are some distinct structural characteristics to understand. There are obviously two main components that could be involved in the aberration/ lameness:

1. The bones/joints (*compression problems*)

2. The soft tissue (*suspension problems*).

Generally horses are observed trotting in a straight line or in a circle to determine lameness. The trot is the most balanced gait the horse has and is useful in highlighting any imbalances in the movement.

When the horse is moving in a circle at a trot there are some simple rules to identifying lameness caused by ***weight bearing***:

1. The horse **will un**-weight the painful part when it is being used. If this part is in the rear it will shift its weight forward by bobbing the head down when the painful part is weight baring. If it is in the front it will raise the head when the painful part is weight baring. (I'm saying part here because the pain could be from a shoulder or a pelvic problem.) The key here is to first see the head movement associated with the weight transfer and then to see how it is timed with the legs as they are being weighted. This is not something that is easy to learn from reading an article;

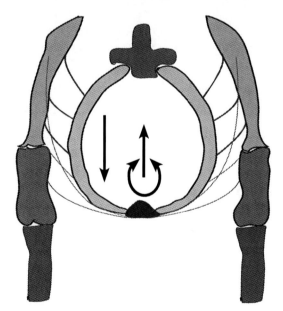

Figure 8. *The horse's thorax will rotate when moving in a circle. Circling to the right will cause more weight to be carried in the right leg and less weight to be carried by the left leg.*

> *As the leg moves through the stance, protraction and retraction phases, it experiences different stresses and accelerations/decelerations.*
>
> *Stance phase is that time when the leg itself isn't moving, but the body is moving over the leg and creating compression stresses in the joints. The transfer of this kinetic energy shows up as a vibration in the soft tissue, much like the vibration in a guitar string. The Check Ligaments in the lower legs both arrest the downward migration of the deep flexor tendon and the fetlock and dampen the vibration that occurs in the tendon as it is shortening from an* **eccentrically** *contracting muscle.*
>
> *Protraction is almost completely accomplished by soft tissue. Except for the flexion and extension of the joints, there is no other compressional strain. It is limited by the soft tissue's ability to lengthen and the joints anatomical barriers. Soft, deep surfaces put more strain on the soft tissue as it protracts.*
>
> *Retraction is fairly harsh in its affects; it has to stop the acceleration of the protracted limb and accelerate it in the opposite direction. When the foot is about to hit the ground the extensors work to slow down the retraction. As the foot hits the ground there is a time lag until the muscles can respond to help support the limb. During this time, all of the stress is on the boney/ligamentous structures of the leg. Ground that does not allow sliding to occur accents this sudden jolt.*

you have to watch a lot of horses under the direction of person who knows what they are looking for, to learn to see lameness.

2. Because the horse does not bend easily when moving in a circle—remember the plains and all that evolution stuff—it will have a rotation in its thorax while moving in a circle **Figure 8**. This translates to more weight being put on the structures on the inside of the circle and less on those on the outside. (Try this for yourself, get down on all fours and play horsey moving in a circle and see where your weight is, or just run around a track and see which foot is weighted more). Knowing this helps you differentiate which part is hurting by correlating the movement aberration with the leg that is on the ground, when it is on the inside of the circle or the outside.

A corollary to this is that the *bones/joints* are being weighted more on the inside of the circle and the *soft tissue* is strained more on the outside. If you correlate a head bob with the outside leg it could be a soft tissue problem. If you have the horse trotted in the other direction, which puts the former outside leg on the inside, and the problem goes away then it probably is soft tissue. (The horse exhibited a lameness only when the leg was on the outside of the circle.)

(I would consider violating my only grade one lame rule for this horse, because the problem is probably soft tissue related.)

This is an example of where in the description of grade two lameness it says *"...aberration is apparent under* **certain** *circumstances..."*, in this case the circumstance is when the leg is on the outside of the circle, but not the inside.

3. There are defined times during the stride, *protraction, landing, support/stance, retraction* that put stress on different components of the structure. Seeing and correlating when the un-weighting occurs helps determine what the problem may be.

4. Bones and joints are stressed more by hard surfaces and soft tissue is stressed more by soft surfaces. The rear end is strained more going uphill and the front more going downhill. A grade one lameness examination may include using different surfaces to try and narrow the problem to a particular circumstance.

Complicated isn't it? Refer to the veterinarian when there is any doubt about what you are seeing. Equine veterinarians have a host of tools they can apply to help narrow the horse's problem down for a proper diagnosis. At no time should you try and diagnose what is happening with the horse. It is easy to let the owner know that you see something that is beyond the scope of your training and that you feel it is in the best interest of the horse to call a veterinarian.

The horse will be grateful to you and the owner will respect you more for your honesty.

Screw Home, occurs in the rear leg, at the stifle, when the tibia and femur come together. There is rotation of the femur that occurs before the joint closes. (This occurs in humans as well) Excessive rotation could indicate a problem in the hock. Refer to a veterinarian.

Quality of Gait

As mentioned above there are different phases of the stride that provide us with information that can be used to determine a strategy for working with the horse. The quality of the gait is determined by the positions of the legs and feet during these different phases.

Let's look at an example of some questions to ask for the trot at the

As the horse's leg is moving it will go through 4 distinct movement stages:

Protraction—**Figure 9**, the leg is moving forward. Protraction ends the retraction phases

Retraction—**Figure 10**, the leg is moving rearward. Retraction ends the protraction phase.

Landing—the foot strikes the ground and starts to load. It is still being retracted.

Stance/Support—**Figure 11**, the instance in the movement when the leg is not moving forward or rearward. The columnar structures are loaded heavily until the soft tissue can respond to provide more support. The body is still moving forward and the retracting tissue is still working.

For both the front and rear legs we want to see equal movement in protraction and retraction: like a pendulum swinging.

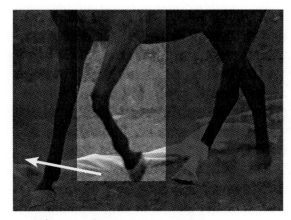

Figure 9 *Protraction Phase*

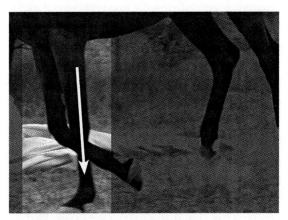

Figure 10 *Stance Phase*

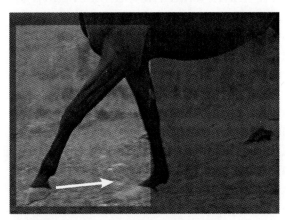

Figure 11 *Retraction Phase*

different phases of the gait:

Protraction

Front leg:

Is the leg moving forward in a straight line throughout this phase or deviating from side to side?

How well does the leg fold? In other words, is the flexion of the leg clean or does the humerus or radius move sideways?

Does the head stay level as the front foot is moving forward?

Does the shoulder move freely?

Rear leg:

Is leg moving forward in a straight line?

How much action is there in the hock?

How far forward does the leg come before it stops?

How much movement is from the leg at the hip and how much from the rounding of the back?

Does the head stay level as the rear leg is moving forward?

Do the angulations of the front and rear leg at the end of protraction appear to be the same? See **Figure 13**.

Landing

On landing does the foot touch down toe first, heel first or flat?

Does the rear foot track into the front foot's footprint, in front of it or behind it?

Is the rear foot landing off to one side of the front foot's print?

Does the head stay level as the feet land?

Do the front and rear feet land at the same time, in a trot?

Is there any interference between the front and rear feet when landing?

Do you hear clicking of foot-on-foot or evidence of scuff marks on the front heels?

Support/Stance

Does the leg come back into full extension, both front and rear?

Or does the leg wobble in partial flexion?

Is there excessive wobble as the bones come together into the support/stance phase?

Does the head stay level through the support/stance phase?

How far is the downward migration of the fetlock?

Is the fetlock downward migration equal side to side?

Is there excessive screw-home in the rear leg?

Is the shoulder free?

Retraction

Front leg:

Does the leg fold up completely and evenly?

Does the shoulder move freely?

How long does the leg stay in

extension?

Rear leg:

Is there a smooth transition or toe dragging?

Is there excessive hock action?

Does the leg fold evenly?

Does the foot land in the front footprint, in front of it or behind it?

Is the rear foot landing off to one side of the front foot's print?

Does the head stay level as the feet land?

In a trot, do the front and rear feet land at the same time?

A Typical Evaluation

Here's a typical *time at the office* for me. I use all of what's been covered before in one way or another. I thought it would help you to put it more into some context.

I have the handler move the horse at a walk while I "listen" to the footfalls and view the quality of the walk.

I look for the following:

Does the horse reach out and have over-stride or is it dragging its toes?

How does the horse carry its head? Is it moving freely?

Is there an undulation in the horse's back?

Does the horse's barrel swing side to side?

Is the horse interested in what it is doing or is it asleep?

This is the time to also gauge the handler's relationship with the horse.

Determine if you will be safe with this horse and handler.

Then I ask the handler to walk the horse and stop. I like them to do it at least five times, walk; stop, so I can see if a pattern emerges in how the horse stops. **Table 1**.

Next I want to see the horse move in a twenty meter circle, or a normal lunge line length, at a minimum three times to the left and three to the right. First at a walk, to evaluate the walk without the handler leading it, then at a trot to determine if the horse is lame. In the circling trot we are looking for the same quality of motion indicators that we used at the walk. We are also looking for how *engaged* the horse's movement is.

Once we have decided to work with the horse, because it is not lame, we want to evaluate it standing again. Have the handler simply hold the horse and let the horse pick its most comfortable stance. Do a general conformation analysis; you'll need to study this elsewhere.

Does it weight all legs equally?

Does the neck come out from the body cleanly?

Is the neck centered?

Is the body balanced, posturally and conformationally, in neck, thorax and rear end?

Sense the overall impression of the horse again.

Are the hamstrings overly large, pushing into a restricted shoulder? (I like to use the analogy of pushing a wheelbarrow with a flat tire. The legs will become overly developed from this activity.)

Is there a tissue *band* in front of the shoulders, making this area look hollow or indented?

It is important to learn to periodically step back from the horse during the session to allow it to integrate the information you've given it, and for you to evaluate the changes. If you wait until the end of the session to see how things are going you'll miss many learning opportunities. And, just as importantly your client, the horse, will not have had an opportunity to adjust to the changes.

Don't become too intense, when you are looking—don't get into your predator mode—it may cause the horse to hide its problems from you.

When you are done, no more than 45 min. of work, have the horse trotted on a circle again and see what has changed.

Standing Analysis

The standing analysis is done twice: once before the horse is trotted in a circle for the first time, and after the initial trot evaluation. The first time, before I see the horse trot, I will not touch the horse. I simply get an idea of the horse's posture and conformation. After I see the horse trot and determine that I'm going to work with it, I do the second standing analysis. This time I will palpate the horse and determine if there are any obvious conformational/postural fixations or holding patterns that I can detect with my hands.

I'll use this second standing analysis to verify what I saw in the movement analysis. In particular, posturally, I want to see how the horse stands with its rear legs. There are three positions the rear legs can be in relative to each other **Table 1**. A propensity to chose only one way of positioning the rear legs can indicate issues with the pelvis. The horse in **Figure 12** is standing with his right rear leg back. He consistently picks this stance and has a problem in his pelvis—the squiggly arrow.

Let's take a look at the horse in **Figure 12** and note any postural issues that may clue us to something we can help—or more importantly—something we may want to enhance. This is one of my horses, so I see him everyday. Don't expect that you'll have as much detail as I'm about to present about him for a horse that you are seeing for the first time.

I've already pointed out that he's standing with his right rear leg back. He's standing square in front with nice tissue length along his top line. Both front legs are fully back in extension, his shoulder is free, the white arc indicates the top of the scapula and the black arc the top of the withers.

What really calls out with this horse is the amount of tension in the rear end, especially in the quadraceps, white arrow. I drew a black line from the point of the hip to the point of the butt to give you some idea of the angulation of this side of the pelvis. The small black arrow shows the direction the pelvis has to move in order to balance the rear end. (We'll discuss this much more in the next book.) It may appear that the hamstrings are tight on this horse because he's not bringing the right rear leg forward; I think that the rotation in the pelvis has confused his muscle stretch receptors and in fact his nervous system *thinks* he's standing square behind! This will create foot landing timing issue when he moves.

I have checked his back and there is no heat where the sacroiliac ligaments are, the squiggly arrow. If you were working with this horse, that would be something for you to do as well; heat in this area can mean an injury. This especially true in pastured horses, slipping in the mud or snow and in jumpers. Exuberant horses running and slipping in the mud or snow can damage this joint. Heat here is a sign to call the veterinarian.

LF	RF	LF	RF	LF	RF
LR	RR		RR	LR	
		LR			RR

Square	**Left Back**	**Right Back**

Table 1 *Possible Positions of the rear legs while standing. Right rear (RR). Left rear (LR).*

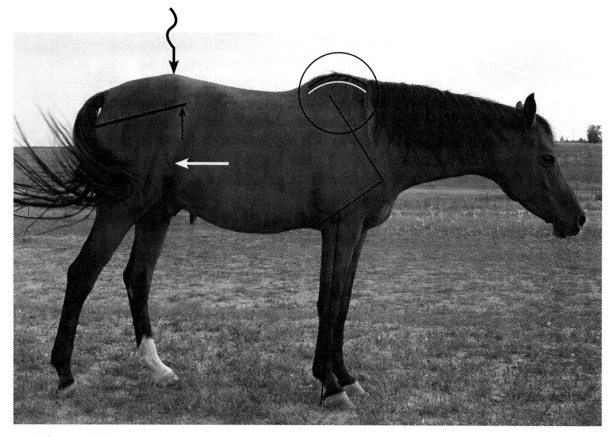

Figure 12 *Analysis of the horse standing. He is standing with RR back.*

Movement Analysis

After I've seen the horse in standing, walking and stopping, I want to see it move at a trot. Up to this time I haven't touched the horse, since I don't know if I'm going to work with it or not. (If I judge that the horse is lame and needs a Veterinarian, then I'm not going to work with the horse.)

I want to see the horse trot in a twenty meter circle with as little interference from the handler as possible. (The best situation for this is to use a round pen.) I want to see the horse go around the circle at least three times in each direction.

At first I will get a *feel* for how the horse moves, kind of an outline of the body. Do the legs all seem to land the same way, load and then retract the same? Or, does something break up that rhythm?

Then I will allow any head movement to come into my awareness. Is the horse bobbing its head up or down at some point? If the answer is yes then I will focus more on the timing of the bob and try and correlate it to a particular leg. At this point, I am thinking that I'm not working with this horse and a veterinarian should be called. As I mentioned before I don't work with lame horses. I prefer that they be referred to me by a veterinarian.

Assuming the horse isn't head bobbing lame, I continue looking at the quality of the trot. How free is the horse's body? Does it undulate with movement or is it held still? How much movement is there in the rear? Do the buttocks move up and down with the leg protraction/retraction or are they held flat? How far into the front foot print does the rear foot land, how much over stride does the horse have?

I look at the attitude of the horse. Is it happy to work or sullen about it? Does the horse pay attention to the handler or not?

The next pages are of my horse moving at a trot and a canter. It is impossible to learn to see horse movement from photos, especially stills. I put these here to better illustrate the words. I chose pictures that are closer to real life than set ups of a horse moving for the camera. Please make an opportunity to spend time with people who know how to look at horses to sharpen your skills. Looking at these pictures and thinking you know how to see horses from them is like listening to Eric Clapton play guitar and thinking you know how to play. You can learn what to look for from the pictures—it is not a useless exercise. But to learn to play with it you'll have to pick up the instrument and practice with it.

Gaits of the Horse

4   2   Walk. Right Rear
Start.
3   1   4 Beats.

2   1   Trot
2 Beats
1   2

4   3   Left Lead
Gallop
1   2   4 Beats

1   2   Pace
2 Beats
1   2

2   3   Right Lead
Canter
1   2   3 Beats

3   2   Left Lead
Canter
2   1   3 Beats

4   3   Right Lead
Gallop
2   1   4 Beats

Here are the most common gaits of the horse. I'm purposely not including too many words in this list, to give you the opportunity to look at the illustrations and make your own mental model for seeing them.

There are a couple of things about horse gaits that are important:

1. Timing: timing of the footfall is important to the quality of the gait. If the gait is two beat you should hear two beats and you should see two beats. If the gait is four beats you should hear and see four equally spaced beats.

2. Rating: the horse should move at the same speed through the gait. If there is a special circumstance that makes them slow down or speed up, make note of that.

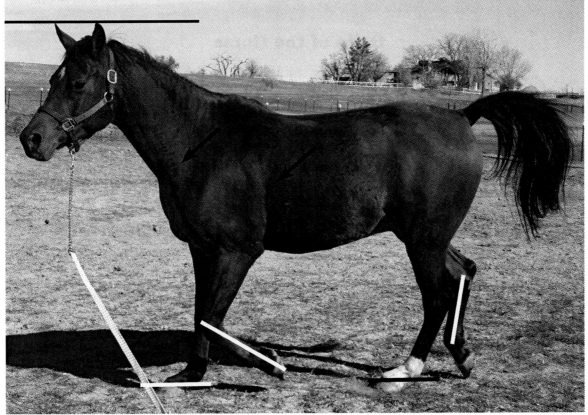

Figure 13 *Trotting to the left. First beat.*

The Trot is the most stable of the gaits. It consists of two beats with the diagonal leg pair moving up at the same time and landing at the same time as shown on the last page. The following figures look at the trot.

Figure 13 shows the first beat of a trot sequence. The white lines on the two legs in protraction are to highlight the two diagonal legs and to give you an idea of how much flexion there is in the leg. I like to look at the flexion and extension to get a gauge of how much the horse is working. This guy's not working hard.

The black line above the head is there to help assess the different head position between this photo and the next one. (More about the relative head position on the next page.)

The black arrows point to the Brachiocephalicus and Latisimus Dorsi that have to work together to move the front limb. With the horse carrying his head this way I would suspect a problem with the Brachiocephalicus. That suspicion is proved wrong in **Figure 15**.

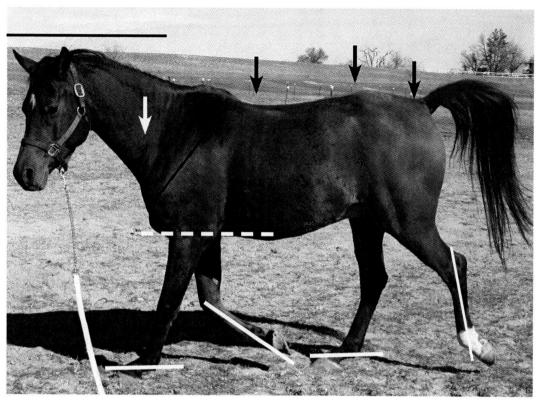

Figure 14 *Trotting to the left. Second beat.*

The first thing we notice in **Figure 14** is the position of the head relative to where it was in the last figure.

This would be significant if it weren't for the way the horse carries himself in **Figure 15**. However, this is what a *head bob* would look like if it continued by being raised when the other diagonal pair were being used. If it were a head bob it would have to be investigated further, using the logics explained earlier for lameness.

The white arrow at the shoulder points to the Brachiocephalicus that is now relaxed as would be expected. The first black arrow, at the withers, points to the bunching of the *Longissimus Dorsi*. I would probably want to palpate this during the session to validate if it is hypertonic.

The next black arrow (moving right) points to a sacral bump, which could be a problem. The third one points to a flattening of the *gluteal fascia*.

The lines at the fetlocks indicate how much flexion there is in these joints, which also indicates how much the flexors have lengthened. Finally the dashed line at the chest show the position of the chest in this figure as opposed to where it will be in **Figure 15**.

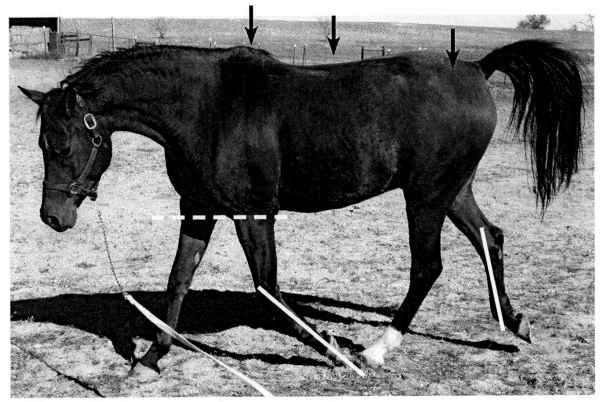

Figure 15 *Trotting to the left. Third beat.*

igure 15 shows the horse in the third stride of the trot, which is a repeat of stride one. (These photos were taken with a camera on a high shutter speed, but it missed the interim suspension phase between stride one and two and two and three.)

I see in this figure is that the horse has taken a more collected posture, with neck telescoping and a longer top line. The head is further down and relaxed, the withers have risen (first black arrow), the thorax is higher (dashed line) and the back has come up (second black arrow). All of these are signs of the *Center of Gravity* being moved towards the rear.

There is still a flattening around the gluteal area that I want to address (third black arrow front to back).

The next three pictures are for you to practice with. **Figure 17** is half way through stride one and two. The right foreleg is breaking over (white line) in protraction. I want to call your attention to the arrows in **Figures 16** and **17**. They point out areas that are hollow, the right arrow in 16, or lengthening, the left arrow in both figures.

Practice Photo

The right arrow points out the hollow area, where the tissue is not lengthening. The left arrow points to the tissue lengthening. The line on the neck highlights the "ewe" neck posture. This posture is to compensate for the tissue not lengthening in the back, by bringing the head closer to the rear end. (The two end points are brought closer together.)

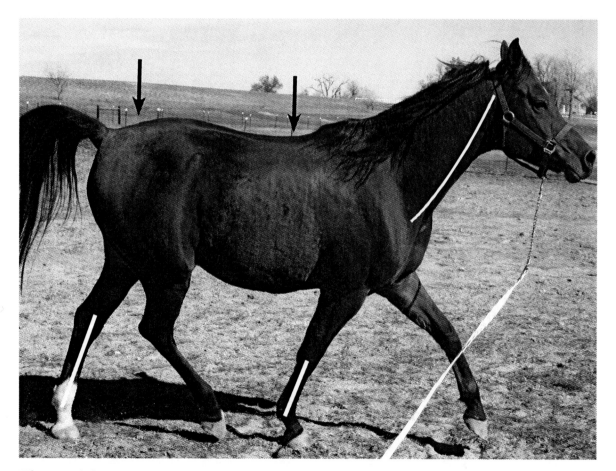

Figure 16 *Trotting to the right. First beat is ending and second's about to land.*

Practice Photo

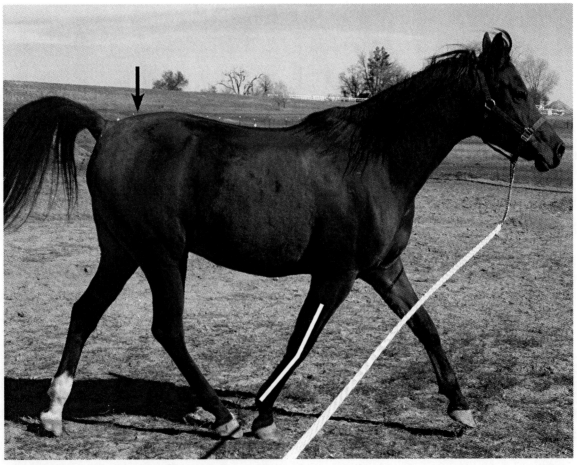

Figure 17 *Trotting to the right. One and half beat.*

Practice Photo

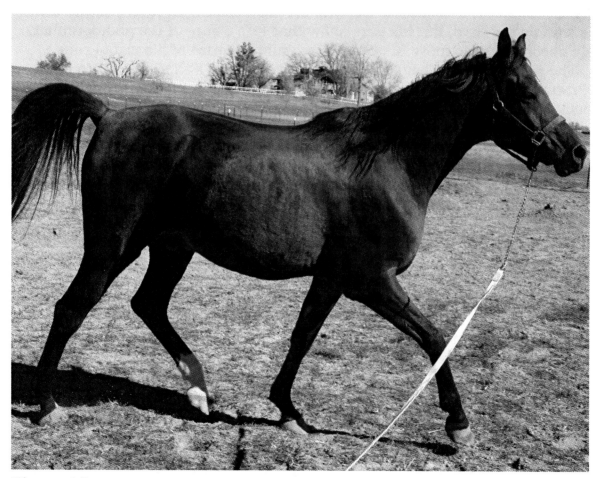

Figure 18 *Trotting to the right. Second beat.*

The Canter

The Canter is a Three Beat Gait, with six parts to it: Beat One/Part One the rear foot lands, the other legs are off the ground. Beat Two/Part Two, the diagonal pair of feet land. Part Three the body moves forward over the diagonal pair, there are three feet on the ground. Beat Three/Part Four the *Leading Foot* lands while the other three are retracted, there are four feet contacting the ground. Part Five, the leading leg supports all of the weight as the other legs are off the ground. Part Six, all feet are off the ground the body is in suspension.

Figures 19 - 21 illustrate of the principles that have been presented so far.

In **Figure 19** Canter Beat One shows a horse Cantering on a left lead, his right rear foot is at Beat 1 of the Canter. (He's coming in from pasture and is leading the herd, but his ears show that he's aware of the photographer. He doesn't have to move his head to see him because of his visual range.)

The right front and left rear legs are in retraction and are about to land. (Protraction is stopped by retraction, while retraction moves through to the back stride and includes the stance phase.)

The left front is in protraction with the Brachiocephalicus—the black line—contracting *concentrically* and the Latissimus Dorsi—the oval—contracting *eccentrically*. The dashed white lines and dashed oval show the position of the Scapula, the Humerus and the Radius (top to bottom). The white lines on the right front and left rear legs should be parallel, indicating the timing is right. If they were greatly different I would suspect that there's a timing/tissue length issue, probably in the hamstrings—black arrow—which have to elongate to allow the rear leg to come forward. In this picture the hamstrings are contracting bringing the leg backward. (A timing issue will result in a 4 Beat Canter, with the two diagonal feet hitting at a different time.)

Don't forget, when looking at these Figures, that the horse is moving forward even if the analysis is static.

The white arrow points to a *False Retinacula* or tissue buildup.

⌃2	⌃3	Right Lead		⌃3	⌃2	Left Lead
		Canter				Canter
⌃1	⌃2	3 Beats		⌃2	⌃1	3 Beats

Stance Phase ●   Retraction ◉   Protraction ○

Figure 19 *Analysis of Movement Canter Beat 1*

The Canter Beat Two

In **Figure 20,** beat two of the canter, the diagonal pair have landed and are supporting the body. The left front—the lead leg—is in retraction. The white arc indicates the shortness in the flexor compartment of the left leg as it brings the leg back into flexion. There is a dynamic timing balance between the extensors and the flexors, with both having to be available to take up the shock of the foot landing on the joints, as the leg moves into the stance phase and takes up more of the weight of the body moving over it. The front limbs lack the angulation of the rear limbs, as such the musculature has to absorb more of the shock on the joints as the joints come into the stance phase. In retraction the extensors are in an eccentric contraction while the flexors are in concentric contraction. When the flexors are unable to come completely out of their contraction (see the stretching chapter for more on this) there will be a slight flexion remaining in the front legs. It will also show up as flexors that feel hard to the touch.

The energy from the rear is moving out of the head—white arrow—as the neck starts to telescope.

The dashed lines show the position of the scapula spine and humerus.

There is a little bit of a delay in getting the right rear leg off the ground. This may be caused by a problem in the sacrum—the upper black arrow points at the sacrum, while the lower black arrow points at the foot—which is visible as a *bump*. If the *illia* doesn't rotate fully due to a mechanical difficulty in the *sacroiliac* joint, the hamstrings will not fire on time because the nervous system reporting is off. (See the chapter on stretching.) The muscles can lose their mechanical advantage or leverage and strength of contraction if there is a lack of full rotation in the *illia*. If this is the case, the horse may drag the toe on the affected side when protracting it.

Notice how far the left rear fetlock has translated towards the ground when compared to the right front. This is an indication of the weight being shifted to the rear.

I put a white line at the level of the pectorals to show how far they have translated relative to the elbow of the right leg. (You want to look at the elbow of the right leg, not the left, since the left is in retraction.)

The white arcing arrow on the rear end indicates the direction the Hamstrings are pulling the rear legs; both rear legs are in retraction. They are being helped by the energy stored in the *lumbar aponeurosis* which in turn is being stabilized by the contraction of the latissimus dorsi.

Stance Phase ●

Retraction ◉

Protraction ○

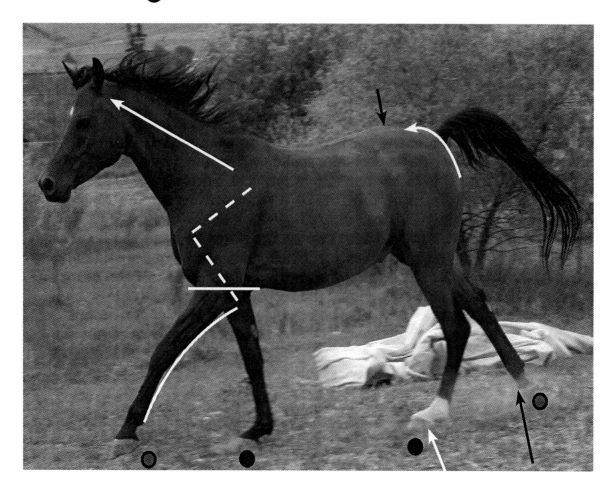

Figure 20 *Analysis of Movement Canter Beat 2*

The Canter Beat Three

The horse in **Figure 21** is supporting all his body weight on the left front leg, with the leg in stance phase and his body—Center of Mass— still propelled forward. Without a rider keeping him *round* he's able to adapt to this weight on the leg, by tightening the *Cervical Serratus* and the *Complexus*—upper white line—thereby bringing the head closer to his rear-end. This is a very simple and energy efficient way to move the COG toward the rear. It also provides more tissue length along the top line. (In the analysis of the trot this was pointed out when the horse "ewed" his neck to do this, figure 16. In the canter there is another nervous system program in effect and therefore another adaptation.)

The *Brachiocephalicus*—lower white line—is in *eccentric contraction*, which brings the nose up as it pulls its cranial attachment down.

The white arrow at the shoulder indicates the *Scalenes* which are in *concentric contraction*.

There is a problem with the right rear leg—arrow on ground—in that it is not being fully folded and the toe is dragging on the ground. This could be indicative of a *Hock* or *Stifle* problem, a shoeing problem or a back problem, in this case I think it is in his back as mentioned before (page 26).

(The Hock and Stifle move together as a reciprocating apparatus. To see what the stifle is doing—flexing/extending—look at the hock, they'll have the same angulation. I put a white line on the photo to show the hock angle, flip this line 180 degrees, as shown in black, and you have the stifle angle.)

The white line at the chest/elbow shows how far downward the thorax has migrated. The squiggle arrow shows the top of the scapula and how high it has moved on the withers. This, hopefully, gives a feel for the amount of mobility that has to be available in the shoulder complex to accommodate these motions.

Stance Phase ●

Retraction ◉

Protraction ○

Figure 21 *Analysis of Movement Canter Beat 3*

A note: I benefitted from being able to blow these photos up to 400% to better see all of this. So, don't think this is what you would see as the horse ran by you.

When you are evaluating the moving horse you will have them circle around you, or trot away and or towards you on a lead with a handler. When they are circling me I like to pick one or two things to look for on each circle or series of strides.

One other piece of advice that comes from Dr. Rolf is to remember that what you see, the map, is not always the same as what you feel with your hands, or the territory. One has to be willing to throw out any treatment strategy that was developed from seeing the horse move and give preference to what you feel under your hands.

Those of you who ride know that this was by no means an exhaustive description of the canter and all of its possible movement aberrations. For this you should consult a dressage book.

Chapter Contents

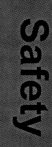

Safety

Safety

Saying a little about safety seems to be appropriate. As the practitioner you are responsible for your and your client's safety while you are working. This means that you need to assure that the place where you work, the person handling the horse for you, if any, the horse you are working on, all of these are contributing to a safe session.

Working with a Handler

It is unfortunate but true that the use of someone to handle the horse, usually the owner, is potentially the most dangerous situation. This is due to a number of reasons:

1. The owner and horse have already established a *herd* relationship, which could be dysfunctional. The owner may not be the dominant animal in this herd which could lead to problems with the horse.

2. The bad safety habits of both the owner and horse are a part of their relationship. They are both use to this, perhaps, unsafe relationship. (I know that I have this kind of relationship with my horse, where I allow him to enter into my space in a way I don't allow

horses I am working with to.)

3. There are three animals involved, rather than two if you are working alone with the horse. This adds to your potential for distraction as well as to that of the owner and horse.

When you enter into this—owner as handler—relationship it is important that the two of you agree on the rules for safety. You don't have to insist on your rules, you do have to agree that there will be some rules. To keep the three of you safe.

There are some things to observe about the handler:

Are they wearing gloves, so they won't be injured if the horse pulls the lead line through their hands? (Having a lead ripped through your hands by a horse that is pulling back is a very painful experience.)

Is the handler attentive to the horse while allowing it space?

Are they playing with the horse or handling it?

Are they wearing safe shoes, that can protect their feet if the horse inadvertently steps on them? (You should also be wearing safe shoes that will protect your toes. Not steel toed safety shoes but not sandals either.)

Is the halter put on with the buckle completely closed? **Figure 1**

If they are using a rope halter, is the tail end of the rope out of the horse's eye?

Figure 1A *Correct*

Figure 1B *Incorrect*

Is the lead rope looped in their hand or coiled around it? Can they let go of the horse if it bolts or will they be caught by the lead and taken along?

Is the lead being managed or laying around on the ground?

Make sure that the handler is always on the same side of the horse as you. This is to assure that a horse that moves will be moving away from you and not have its rear turned into you!

Anybody who has had a horse pull back and break a halter knows how hard it is to re-train them to stand while tied.

The reason most halters break when the horse pulls back is because they are not being used correctly.

In Figure 1 A the halter buckle is being used correctly. The pressure on the belt will be taken up and distributed through the buckle to the rest of the halter.

In Figure 1 B the buckle is not being used correctly, all of the pressure will be on the "nail" the weak link in the halter. The horse can pull back and bend or break this nail and the halter will fail!

Tying the Horse

Tying the horse presents its own set of safety issues. Here are some of the things to be aware of:

Is the thing the horse is tied to stable or will the horse be able to pull it out?

Is the thing the horse is tied to going to hurt you or the horse if the horse pulls it out? (I have a *D Ring* nailed in to a post in my barn that I tie to. It is held in place by two small nails, that the horse can easily pull out. If the horse pulls

Having the horse be able to pull out the thing they are tied to can be desirable. For instance if the horse is tied to a post in the barn, being tied to something that will pull out rather than pull down the barn post is desirable.

On the other hand the horse will be loose in the barn with the thing they pulled out attached to the end of the lead line. (This is how my barn is set up.) You need to be aware that this potential issue exists.

Many barns use cross ties to secure the horse for grooming and tacking up. These aren't the best for our work. For one they don't let the horse move enough, and cross ties are usually associated with tacking up, which can be a negative association for the horse. If you are working in cross ties check to see if there is a breaking string (usually some bailing twine) between the tie and the post, this will allow the horse to get free if they pull hard on the tie.

this out, that D Ring will be at the end of a flailing lead rope!)

Do you know how to untie the knot they used? Is the knot one that is appropriate for a horse, i.e. one that won't tighten when pulled on by the horse, making it impossible to untie in an emergency situation?

In one of my classes, with some very horse savvy people, one set of students tied the horse to a stall door.

Have you ever been in a barn when a horse that was tied to a stall door shied, pulled the door off the wall and came through the barn with the door attached to it? I have and it is very scary. Not to mention bad for the door.

Cross Ties

Sometimes the handler will stay with you while they put the horse in cross ties. This is a very convenient arrangement but one that can lead to less vigilance on the part of the handler. In fact, the cross ties may free up the handler so much that they become more of a distraction to the horse and you.

When the horse is in cross ties, you may want to proceed as though the handler is not, there as a handler, to help you if something happens. You can ask the handler to step back a safe distance from the horse so they are not tempted to correct the horse should it move.

Another problem with cross ties is that the horse has been trained not to move around while they are in them. Horses are not in cross ties for fun they're there to get groomed and tacked. This discipline can detract from the horse's ability to move and process the changes that are happening in their body, from your work.

On the other hand you are not there to undo the training the horse has undergone with relation to cross ties. It is a balancing act for you to let the horse move with your work and not just fidget.

Along the same lines cross ties are places where other horses are brought to groom, you don't want to be working next to another horse that is being groomed. It is too distracting for you, your handler and the client horse.

Not Tying

The other option is to not tie the horse at all. This is the one I opt for when I am in a place that contains the horse, i.e. a round pen or a stall. In these cases the horse is physically confined to the pen or stall and the only need for the lead is to better direct it for the work.

In these situations I will loop the lead rope around the rail of the round pen or stall bar a few times. This gives me enough time to secure the horse if they are pulling back on the lead.

I will also work with end of the lead rope stuffed in my back pocket or belt if I'm in a closed space. If they get loose there's no place for them to go, so it is pretty safe.

A Safe Environment

Once I was working in a stall with a really nice horse. He was leaning into me while I worked on his hamstrings, and I was leaning against the stall wall. He leaned into me more and I leaned into the wall more... THE WALL STARTED TO BREAK! I was trapped between a horse, who was in la-la land, and the wall that was falling over. Luckily I was able to get the blissed out horse's attention to get him off me.

The moral is: NEVER get between a horse and a hard spot.

The corollary is: Don't trust the strength of barn walls!

Make sure the area where you are working is safe. There should be enough room for a horse to act up without running into something that could hurt them. This is also true for you and the handler; can you get away from the horse with out getting hurt? What I'm saying is to take a good look at your work area. Is there something that will hurt or obstruct the horse or you, if you need to move away quickly?

If the horse rears will it hit the ceiling or a light fixture?

If you are working in the barn alley, are there saddle racks that can get in the way?

Are there hoses, tack boxes and other potential obstacles around?

Is the surface you're working on slippery? Cement and horse shoes are not a good combination.

Are there nails coming out of the walls in the stall you are working in?

Are there buckets laying around?

Can you get away from a 1000 pound horse moving towards you, without getting hurt by something else?

You get the idea:

Be conscious of your safety!

Warning Signs

Possibly as important as being aware of the physical environment you are working in, is being aware of the horse and the clues they are giving you.

Early in the book I mentioned how horses have an expectation that we can see them as well as they can see us. This lack of ability on our part can lead to some problems if they are signalling their dissatisfaction to us and we miss it.

This can also happen with the horse's expectation that we understand all of their language and customs.

Some of the bad signs that a horse can put out are:

Pinning ears - while this doesn't mean the horse is necessarily aggressive; it does warn us that the horse anticipates something aggressive will happen. You want to know which it is.

Swishing a tail - this can happen when there are flies present which means something different. But when it happens in coincidence with your work, it may mean they are irritated by it.

This can mean that you are working too fast, too deep too fast or that your touch is too tentative and you feel like a fly. In other words irritating!

Stomping a foot - this can be an expression of irritation, like when a fly is on their leg. Or of exasperation with your not hearing them.

Grinding teeth - this is the equivalent to pinning ears to me. It represents a frustrated animal.

Kicking - nuff said?

Biting - same as above. Unless they are mouthy to begin with, which, to me, is more dangerous.

Some of the good signs are:

Sighing - this is often associated with a nervous system release of tension or a holding pattern.

Licking lips - is a sign of contentment and submission as well as "I got it!".

Moaning - this can be a sign of something that feels good or of something that is in that "hurts so good" category. You'll need to get more data to decide where it fits. (I've had this happen a lot while stretching a joint; especially with horses who have chronic joint problems. I don't know if it means

they are getting relief or that it actually hurts more. Once a horse sounded like it was "crying". My strategy here is to step away from the horse and wait for it to look at me with a "ok, let's go on" type of look. Not too scientific but it works for me.)

Yawning - some people think this is a release of toxins, I don't know what it means, other than perhaps the horse is relaxed.

Blinking - this one is more obvious when the horse is moving. It means the horse is submitting to what ever you are asking of it. It doesn't mean that you are dominant to the horse, other than for that moment you are in control.

Be careful about allowing the horse to get too close to you with its mouth. It might feel spiritually full filling to have a horse breath in your ear, but having one start to nibble on it is not.

Mutual grooming - this is one of those things that horses do with each other. For horses it is probably great, for us it can really hurt. It is not that hard to distinguish mutual grooming from an attack. The attack is fast and hurts. The mutual grooming is slower and can lead to it hurting.

Licking - this usually means the horse sees you as lower in the pecking order and is taking care of you. I'm not sure if that is a good thing or a bad one.

Chapter Contents

Fascial Release Techniques

The techniques used in Equine Myofascial Release have specific uses that are dictated by what the tissue needs. Similar to the brushes of an artist they are not confined to use only where we show them in the technique sections. As you become familiar with them you'll interchange them, and move seamlessly through their usage.

Sweep

Is the movement away from the starting point. For instance if one has the thumbs together, a "sweep" would simply take them apart as illustrated in **Figure 1**.

The thumbs, in this case, have slowly sunk into the tissue and are being drawn apart creating a stretch in the fascia. This stretching of the fascia engages the restrictions to movement. (The other fingers are not anchoring onto the side of the head, they're just resting.) The Sweep can be applied with other parts of the hands and arms, such as knuckles and elbows.

It is important that the stretch be put in two directions simultaneously with any resistance to the stretch being held until it releases.

This is a direct technique, in that the fascial adhesions will be engaged directly and held until they release.

Frontal Sweep

Figure 1 *The Sweep using the thumbs on the frontal bone's fascia.*

Circles and "C" Stroke

These are two very commonly used strokes. **Figure 2**
The circles are an offshoot of the circles technique that Linda Tellington Jones developed for her Tellington Equine Awareness Method (TEAM). Tellington Jones describes their use as being disruptive to the nervous system pattern. I feel they are very effective in breaking up fascial adhesions—if you apply the force in 360 degrees of tissue motion.

For both techniques, one slowly sinks into the fascial layer that is to be addressed and moves the fascia in a circle.

The "C" stroke could be called a subset of the circles. One sinks to the desired fascial layer and takes the tissue through a "C". (I guess you could estimate this as 270 degrees of motion.) For the circle you would take the tissue through 360 degrees.

The direction of the stroke can be either clockwise or counter-clockwise depending on what you feel is needed.

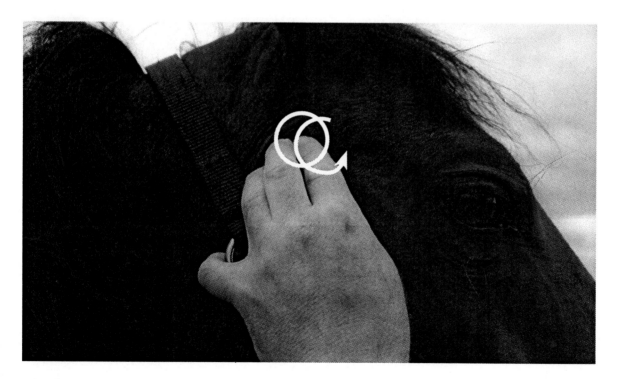

Figure 2 *Circles or "C" Stroke*

Skin Rolling

This both a diagnostic aid as well as an effective intervention to break up fascial adhesions. **Figure 3**

To perform skin rolling one takes up a pinch of skin and rolls it between the fingers in one direction. The adhesions will reveal themselves as a marked slowing of the rolling action.

The adhesions you'll encounter using skin rolling will be between the skin and the superficial fascia. When you encounter an adhesion you can use one of your other tools to address it if it is not resolved by the skin rolling itself. Many times the skin rolling is enough to give the fascia more hydration, which allows it to move. This added hydration and movement often results in more adhesions being removed by the body while moving.

Skin rolling does not address the deeper adhesions in the myofascia but will help to uncover them by removing the more superficial ones.

The skin rolling should be performed in more than one direction to assure to assure you cover all the planes of movement.

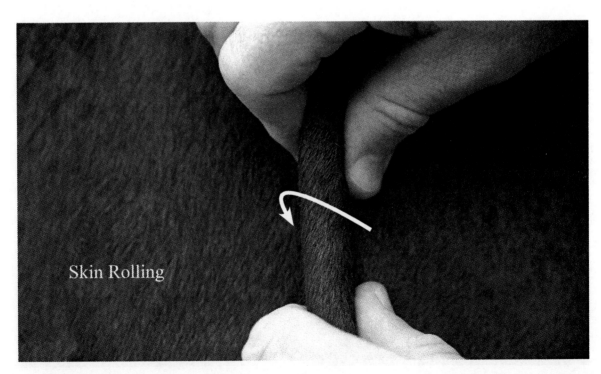

Skin Rolling

Figure 3 *Skin Rolling*

Compression

Remember the exercise in the fascia chapter where you compressed a sponge? Compression is used to move fluid into or out of the tissue. Slowly sink into the tissue until the first barrier is felt, black arrow **Figure 4**. Then shift the movement along the fascial plane, white arrows. The first barrier is held until it releases. The release of the barrier will feel like a softening in the tissue. The movement and pressure is continued until the next barrier is felt. Hold this barrier until it releases and so on.

I like to stop often and step back from the horse to allow it time to absorb the change; and to see the change in the tissue myself.

The nervous system will reset/remove each of the barriers as they are engaged and hydrated. One removes the compressive force very slowly, this prevents a *rebound effect*. The speed that one comes out of the tissue, should be approximately twice that of going into it.

Of course, if one wants to rebound the tissue then come out quickly. Rebounding the tissue can be used where there's been a loss of tone.

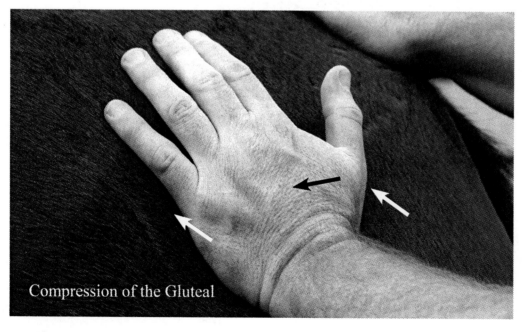

Compression of the Gluteal

Figure 4 *Compression*

Tissue Testing

Engage the fascia at the depth you want to work by slowly sinking down. Then, take fascia through all possible directions of movement. Make sure you are in the facia and not the skin, and that you are at the same depth for each movement.

There will be some directions that move easily and some that have a resistance to movement. The resisted directions are called *barriers*. If you are using a direct technique engage the barrier. If you want to use an indirect technique, engage the areas of ease by taking them more into their movement ease.

Either way, once a barrier has been removed tissue test again to find the next barrier. This is an important point. Once a barrier has been removed other barriers may reveal themselves in another plane of movement. Do not assume that the barriers will be in one direction or available at the same fascial depth.

Figure 5 shows testing in the 4 cardinal directions for convenience of illustration. In reality you can test in many smaller increments.

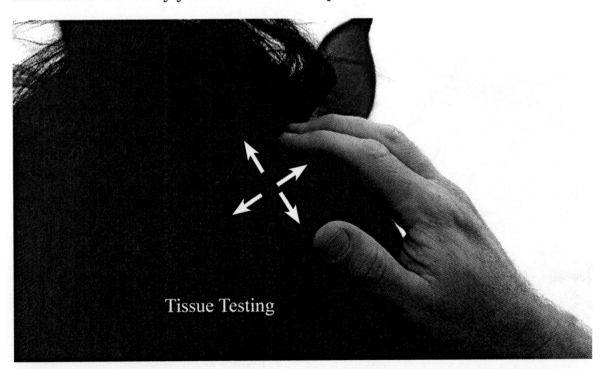

Tissue Testing

Figure 5 *Tissue Testing*

Bending

For lack of a better term I call this technique *Bending*. You can visualize this technique by thinking about how you bend a green stick to break it.

There are two components:

1. **Bending Compression**, illustrated in **Figure 6**.

In bending compression we are applying the force away from our body into the tissue creating a bend in the tissue. The bend of the tissue creates a stretch on the other side, which breaks up the fascial adhesions that may be there.

The fingers on the opposite side of the bend are adding a sweeping component to the tissue.

2. **Bending Distraction**, illustrated in **Figure 7**.

Bending distraction is the opposite component of the bending compression. It creates a stretch on the side we are facing breaking those adhesions. The thumbs are adding a sweeping component to the technique.

I like to use this technique to gain length in tough tissue like ligaments or even a muscle like the semimembranosus. It is always used as part of a treatment for scar tissue. Bending the scar will break the adhesions.

I use this with the Nuchal ligament to break up adhesions between it and the complexus, rhomboid, and etc.... To do this you would feel the separation between the ligament and the other structures and sink your fingers into this space while bending it.

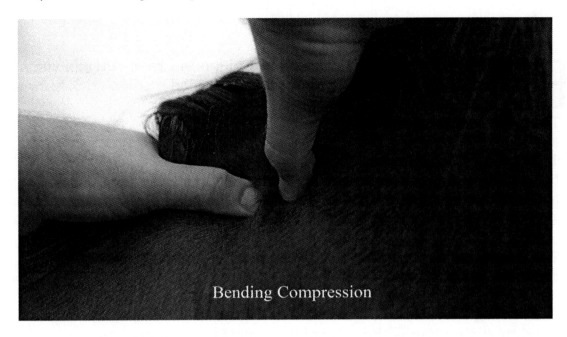

Figure 6 *Bending Compression*

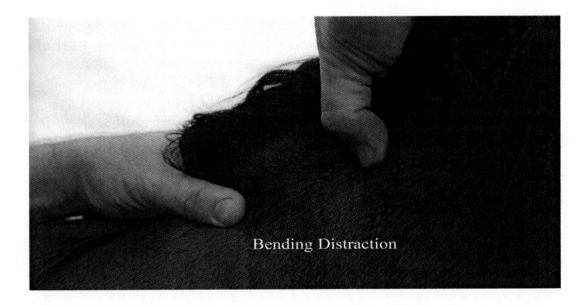

Figure 7 *Bending Distraction.*

Cross Fiber Friction

Cross fiber work is used anywhere length is desired in the tissue. Moving across the fibers is the way to lengthen them.

In cross fiber friction one engages the scar and moves it in different directions to work the random pattern that the scar has formed. This is fairly aggressive in that the scar's adhesions have to be broken. As with any work where the therapy has been to disrupt, an organizing force has to be put in to assure the collagen and elastin are laid down along the proper path. To do this add an organizing stretch of the tissue around the scar when you're done. **Figure 8**

(Cross fiber friction is used to lengthen and aggressively break up scar tissue. Bending compression, is used to re-organize the collagen fibers once the scar is softened.)

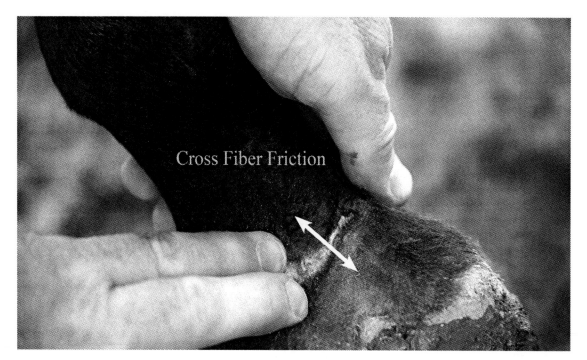

Figure 8 *Cross Fiber Friction*

Chapter Contents

General Approach

Any alarm reactions on the part of the horse is cause to stop and try another approach. The trick is to work a little stop and step back to watch the horse's reaction to the work. Let them process what you're doing because it will be completely new to them.

Sometimes the horse will react to the memory of an old sensation rather then to your work. You'll have to re-educate their nervous system that the touch you are providing is different and therapeutic. Keep two hands on the horse while you are working, this provides a good magnetic, energetic and electric connection between the two of you.

Not all of these techniques would be used with each horse. I'm illustrating them here so you can have them in your tool box when you need them. If they seem redundant study them again. I assure you each one is unique.

The Head

I like to start with the horse's head when I work; specifically the Atlanto Occipital region. Starting here gives me a chance to meet the horse at a place on its body that has been handled by people. The sensation of Myofascial Release is new to the horse, and I'm a new person to the horse. Initially, they don't know if I'm there to help them or not. Also, the head is far from the *business end* if you know what I mean. I can better gauge the reactions of the horse to my work, as well as the handler's reactions to the horse, (in case there's an adverse reaction to the work) while being in a safer place.

While the head is normally handled, halters and bridles on and off, it is not a place where people seem to relate to the horse. This is a shame since it is a place that the horse loves to have handled correctly.

Years ago someone explained to me that the head of a horse is the place where humans and horses can have a special relationship. That it should be kept as a special place that could be used by humans, with our hands, to reward and to bond with the animal. The logic was that horses, not having hands struggle to interact with their heads. They may try to flick a fly off their face/head but they can't reach into their ear and scratch it. And we all know how good that can feel!

Before you start to work the fascia take some time to familiarize yourself with the anatomical landmarks of the head. Find the bones, blood vessels and nerves, from their different tissue feel.

The bones will feel like a bone, sometimes covered with a fascial *Bubble Wrap*. The blood vessels will be softer and have more viscosity to them. They may have a pulse. The nerves will feel like a string or guitar wire if they're compressed, and like a water filled tube if they are inflamed.

There's not a lot of fat on the horse's head and it is easy to pin the tissue, nerves and blood vessels, to a bone. You can avoid doing this by keeping the angle of your fingers and hands oblique to the tissue as you are working.

Many of the muscles in the head are attached to fascial sheets rather than bone and can be detached if you are too aggressive. Go slow and pay attention to the horse's reactions.

Pay particular attention to what you are doing around the zygomatic and mandible bones, these are places where you can inadvertently trap a nerve. USE AN OBLIQUE ANGLE TO YOUR TOUCH AND BE SLOW and GENTLE. Remember speed is the enemy of depth when working with soft tissue.

I don't want to suggest that you shouldn't try and free a nerve that is trapped in a fascial adhesion. I do want to caution you that you need to know your anatomy when working on the head and be able to feel your way through the territory.

If only because there's not as much fat or protective hide as there is in other areas.

When you are in front of the horse, keep one of your feet on their closest foot. If they decide to strike out, not at you but at the sensation they're having, you'll get a warning when the foot moves.

I can't over emphasize the benefit this head work has for the horse. The horse will appreciate you assisting them in freeing their head.

Table 1 provides a list of some of the more common muscles of the head that you will encounter in using these techniques. While it lists muscles, the intention is to work with the fascia that defines them. The muscles are a name for the territory you will be working in. You can see from the naming conventions of these muscles that their action is often included as part of the name, Levator Labii = elevator of the lip.

Muscle Name	Origin	Insertion	Action	Reference Figure
Parotidoauricularis	Parietal Bone	Lateral Ear	Moves Ear	1
Cervicoauricularis	Cervical Bone	Medial Ear	Moves Ear	1
Scutalaris	Frontal Bone	Medial Ear	Moves Ear	2
Levatornasolabialis	Nasal Bone	Nose and Lip	Raise nostril and lip	3
Levator labii Superior	Nasal Bone	Upper Lip	Raises Lip	3
Zygomatic Muscle	Zygomatic	Lip	Raises lip	5
Masseter	Mandible	Zygomatic	Raises Mandible	6

Table 1. *Some common muscles of the head and which technique works with them.*

Atlanto-Occipital Release

While positioned at the side of the horse, use your fingertips to engage the space between the occiput and the atlas. The objective is to very gently encourage more space in the joint by slowly sinking your fingers down as the tissue responds and opens.

You can use your other hand on the halter to bring the horse's head up and down opening and closing the joint and helping to move the tissue under your fingers.

Next gently tissue test behind the AO and engage any barriers until they release. The horse should be dropping its head in acceptance of this procedure. The last stroke should take the tissue away from the AO towards the axis.

Horses that move with their heads held in the air, sky gazing, will have closed this joint. (As will people spending too much time looking up at their computer.) For this closed AO you'll have to use some of the nuchal ligament techniques along with this one.

Repeat from the other side.

Figure 1 *Atlanto Occipital Release*

Frontal Bone Circles

While standing in front of, or to the side of the horse. Use your thumbs or fingertips to engage the fascia on top of the head right between the ears, and make small circles or use a "C" stroke to break up any adhesions.

Be very gentle and slow in your sinking into the restricted layer. This area does not have a lot of fat to cushion your touch, so a *pointy tool* is not advisable.

The horses seem to appreciate this work and will drop their heads while you are doing it. If it doesn't or acts irritated, try changing your pressure. You may be too soft and feel like a fly or too hard with an intense touch. If you decide to stand to one side while releasing this fascia make sure you work from the other side as well. This simply gives the horse a sensation from both sides.

If you work in front of the horse keep one of your feet on top of the horse's foot that is closest to you. This way, if the horse should strike at the sensation they're having, you'll have a warning to move out of the way. (That is two times I've mentioned this. I think it is important.)

Figure 2 *Frontal Circles*

Sweeping the Frontal Bone

This technique will generally relax the horse and let you get to know each other. Believe me a relaxed horse is easier to work on. However, don't confuse a relaxed horse with the one that is not engaged with the process. As you are working the horse will be moving with your work. A horse that is relaxed and moving with your work is a good thing. A horse that is dull and passively avoiding your work is not.

There's a nerve and a blood vessel running down the side of the nose. You should locate them before you start.

Using your thumbs, start at the center of the frontal bone and sweep towards the lateral aspects. You don't have to worry about your moving the bone, you won't. You DO have to sink in slowly and slowly sweep your thumbs apart. This doesn't require force, it requires time to sink into the tissue. Continue this for the entire frontal bone.

Make sure you stay on the bone. When you get towards the nose you'll be engaging the cartilage. You'll know it is cartilage because it has more *give* than bone. You don't want to push into the cartilage.

You'll also want to be careful of the tear ducts as you approach the eye. These run from the eye to the nose and you don't want to impinge on them. You can gently stroke the

Figure 3 *Frontal Sweep*

tear ducts to move any fluid that is stuck in them, especially if the horse has a nasal discharge. Stroke the teat duct towards the nose. There's a fatty pad above the eye you don't need to work there.

Atlanto-Occipital Sweep

The area around the AO joint is like a traffic circle for muscles of the head and neck. The Occipital muscles come in here, the Brachiocephalicus and Sternocephalicus muscles attach here. The muscles of the ear originate here... You can effect all of them from here.

For lack of a better term I called this technique an AO Sweep. **Figure 4**

While positioned on one side of the horse use your fingertips to engage the tissue. Gently, tissue test and engage any barriers until they release. Then using a *sweeping stroke* take the tissue away from the joint. (Always end your work in an area around a joint with a stroke that takes the tissue away from it.)

The horse should be dropping its head in acceptance of this work. If it doesn't, place your hand there and let the horse get used to it. Don't try and accomplish anything other than having your hand there. The horse could be sore in this area. It is one of the spots that a bit—especially leveraged bits—work on. Also, many horses have pulled back on a halter while tied which can make this area sore. Repeat from the other side.

Figure 4 *Atlanto Occipital Sweep*

Sweeping the Zygomatic

I'm using my thumb in **Figure 5**—you don't have to—to sweep the zygomatic tissue. The direction is toward the temple. This will help to open the fascia of the Masseter.

You want to be slow and gentle here as the muscles have a tenuous attachment to the bone. Before you start to move tissue feel the zygomatic bone, it should feel clean like a bone. If you feel a, *bubble wrap* like, textured tissue, that indicates the fascia is wrapping to the bone and not moving. You can hold a constant pressure on this bubble wrap feeling tissue and it will seem to melt under your fingers. An organizing stroke will complete the release.

Remember that any time we work around a bone, WE NEVER PIN TISSUE TO THE BONE! Go slowly, feel your way and feel what's under your hand/fingers. One of the muscles that attaches to the zygomatic is called the *zygomaticus,* it brings the lips back. The Masseter also attaches here. Stop after every stroke and let the horse process the changes.

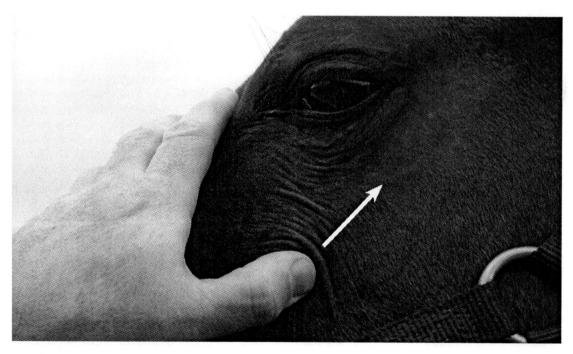

Figure 5 *Zygomatic Sweep*

Mandible Sweep

The tissue around the mandible can become *wrapped* around the bone, giving the bone a *bubble wrap* feeling. This in itself causes a reduction in ROM, and a closing of the space between the left and right mandibular rami. The airway of the horse can be obstructed when the space between the Rami is narrowed by soft tissue. If the horse is asked to come into a vertical headset with a closed airway it could cause the horse to justifiably rebel to keep its nose up and airway clear.

While you need to be definitive in moving the tissue around the mandible you also have to be very aware not to trap the *facial nerve* against the bone. Slow and steady is the best course here. If something feels stringy or the horse reacts, stop and start over. If this area is very sensitive to touch it could indicate that the facial nerve is being impinged. Try to find it and slowly and gently pulse it in coordination with the horse's breathing.

Sweep the mandible clean, starting either superiorly or inferiorly. Stand on one side of the horse while working then switch sides. You may need to hold the head down with one hand gently on the nose. Make sure you work the bone's medial and lateral aspects. (Notice how soft this horse's eye is.)

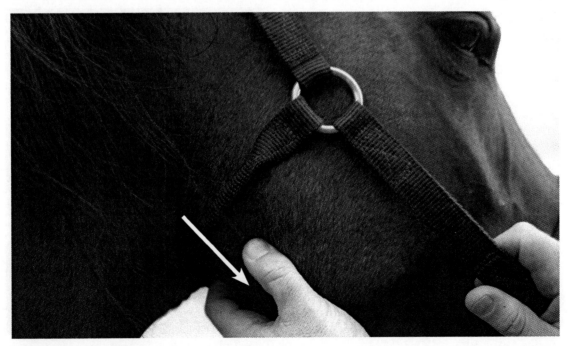

Figure 6 *Mandible Sweep*

Masseter Compression

Releasing the masseter will greatly influence the way the horse responds to the bit. Unfortunately, the heavy-handed rider may not experience the change your work will make, but the horse will. **Figure 7** shows the tissue being swept toward the temple.

You've already engaged part of the masseter with the lateral border mandible sweep. For the first part of this release, engage the fascia layer by layer making circles with your thumbs or fingertips.

You can position yourself in front of the horse, or at one side, or reaching under the neck to the other side while the horse rests its head on your shoulder. (Work from both sides before finishing.)

Once the masseter is relaxed, engage the fascia and tissue test it to determine which way it resists moving. Take the fascia into this resistance and hold until the resistance releases. Continue this for the entire muscle. Make sure you work from both sides.

The *Parotid Gland* borders the masseter's caudal edge (towards the rear). There's no reason to work in that area.

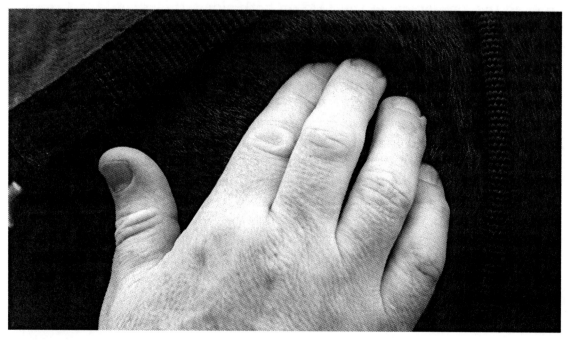

Figure 7 *Masseter Compression*

The Temporal Mandibular Joint (TMJ)

I see a lot of people in my human practice with TMJ problems. Imagine how many more I would see if they had someone holding onto their jaw with a bit and reins! Unbalanced hands on the reins at the end of the bit is more of a problem than the bit is for the horse's mouth. These unbalanced hands set up a torsion in the mandible, and the TMJ takes up most of the strain from the hands of unschooled riders.

That the horse suffers from TMJ issues can be inferred when we find an imbalance in the mandible. In other words, we can assume that the horse with a mandibular imbalance also has a TMJ imbalance and therefore has TMJ issues.

You can check the relative mandible balance by holding the left and right mandibular rami in you fingers and determining if your fingers align horizontally and vertically. I say this is relative because this is a *feeling sense* that you'll have, not an absolute measurement. If you think the mandible is not balanced, you may want to refer the horse to an equine dentist or chiropractor.

An additional (that is additional not another) way to check is to feel the distance in the joint space at the TMJ on both sides, they should feel the same. You can do this easily by putting the sides of your thumbs, similar to **Figure 9,** into the space at the zygomatic arch and gauging how easily and far you can sink into the joint space.

The mandible articulates in two places with the zygomatic arch of the temporal bone, on the medial side and on the lateral side. If you feed the horse something you'll see these articulations as she/he chews.

Engage the fascia and tissue test it. Take the tissue into the restriction and hold until it releases **Figure 8**. Continue to the next barrier, this is accomplished by tissue testing again as above to find the barrier.

If you gently cradle the rami of the mandible in your hands while you are in front of the horse, you will feel a gentle rocking motion in it. It will come down and out towards you and then up and back towards the head. This is the cranial rhythm and its inherent motion on the mandible. This rhythm should cause both rami to move equally, if it doesn't you should work some more to balance it.

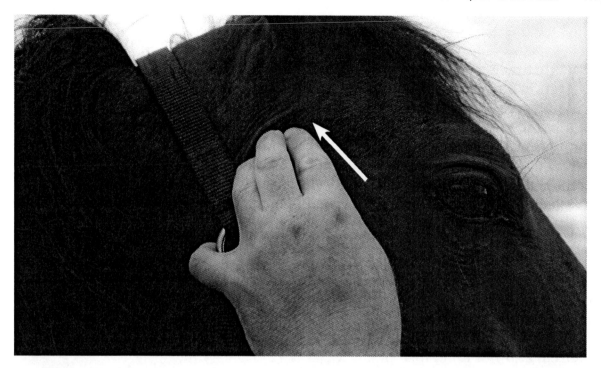

Figure 8 *TMJ Release 1*

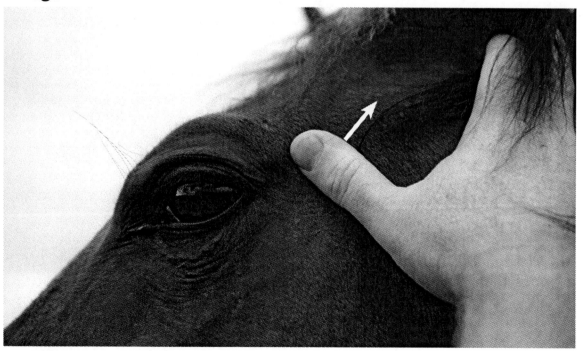

Figure 9 *TMJ Release 2*

Forelock Pull

This technique is not only a useful one for breaking fascial adhesions it is also one that is appreciated by the horse as a tension reliever.

Figure 10 How many times have you combed or brushed the forelock of a horse and had them lower their head in gratitude and submission? How many times have you pulled on your own hair to relieve tension?

You start this technique by taking up as much of the forelock as you comfortably can. Gently pull the forelock away from the head until you can feel the pull-back of the superficial fascia. Once you have reached this point you can slowly take the forelock in a circle while maintaining contact with the fascia. Start by making a small circle and slowly enlarging it to move more of the fascia.

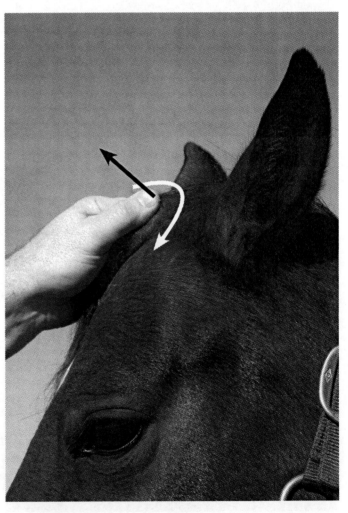

Make sure you are making a circle and not an ellipse or some other shape. If you can't make a circle you are trying to move too much tissue at once, back off and make a smaller circle.

Take the forelock clockwise and counter clockwise. You can also take it up and down if you sense that there's an adhesion in that direction. Sometimes there will be an adhesion in one direction but not in the other.

The horse will appreciate this. Try doing this technique on yourself or someone you like and get some feedback on how it feels. As well as how sensitive your touch is.

Figure 10 *Forelock Pull.*

Ear Circles

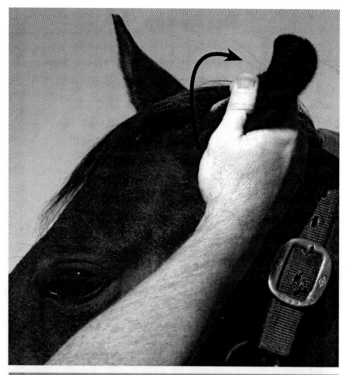

H ere's another technique that the horse will appreciate, if it is done slowly and gently. **Figure 11-12**

A lot of people think that their horse's have been *eared*—when a person uses the ear to inflict pain on the horse as a means to control them—I don't know how often this actually happens, but I hear it a lot.

What I think happens more often is people use the halter as some form of punishment, thereby causing the horse to dislike anything around their ears or poll.

As you can see the horse in these photos doesn't dislike this at all. But, please, be careful around your client's horse and take your time working here.

Circle the ears around their attachment first close to the attachment and then from further away as the horse submits to the feeling. This will break up any small adhesions caused by the halter. This also helps the horse by receiving a new feeling/sensation to associate with in this area.

For safety stand to the side of the horse and keep one foot

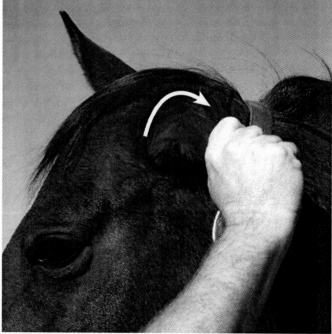

Figure 11-12 *Ear Circles*

Ear Sweep

The Ear Sweep is another treat for a horse. **Figure 13** According to Linda Tellington-Jones the ear should be soft and flexible, similar to a dog's. This technique brings more awareness of the head and ears to the horse. This is a great technique for lowering a horse's pulse and respiration as well as calming the horse under stress.

Begin close to the head, gently sink

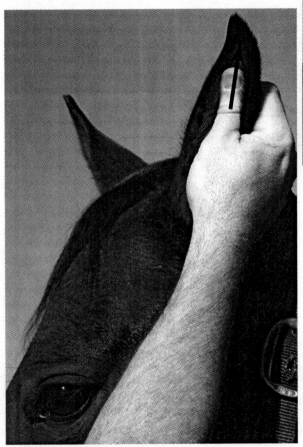

Figure 13 A and B *Ear Sweep*

into the tissue inside the ear, and work this tissue up towards the top of the ear.

You can modify this by doing small C strokes inside the ear as you work your way up the ear. Work inside and outside either together or separately.

The horse should be receptive to this work. If not, then bypass it for something else. You may want to teach this to the owner so they can acclimate the horse to having its ears worked.

Tip of Ear Circles

Continuing with more ear work, **Figure 14,** this technique is another special treat for the horse. It is also one that brings a new sensation to the animal helping to open its mind for further learning.

Try this technique, in fact try all of them, on yourself to see how if feels as you touch with more or less pressure. Remember that the horse can not use a finger to scratch its own head. Imagine what a treat this is to the horse to have someone spend time on these areas that aren't regularly touched. I know that I'm being a little preachy here but my horses love it.

If we subscribe to the logic that the fascia is a unitary element from the top of the head to the feet, then we would not be working all of it if we do not work with the ears.

This technique is a very simple application of C strokes to the tip of the ear. You are feeling for slight adhesions in the superficial fascia covering the ear cartilage. The ear in this area is mostly cartilage and should be flexible. The cartilage is covered by a thin covering of hide and fascia. You will be working both the outside and the inside of the ear with this technique. You can work them separately or at the same time depending on your dexterity.

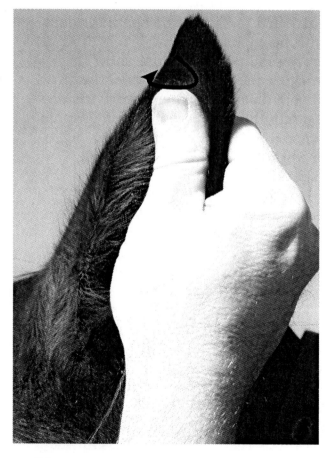

Figure 14 *Tip of Ear Circle*

Mouth Work

Yeah that is right, mouth work! The mouth of the horse is another place that is not related to in a very positive way. Bits, floating of teeth and treats are the only things that most horses have as a relationship between their mouth and their owner/handler.

There are a lot of horses that are considered mouthy because they are uneducated about their mouths. Beyond this, many horses have hardened their mouths against riders with heavy hands.

These illustrations just show working the lips. That is because my fingers disappear when I work inside the mouth and make no photographic sense. I want to encourage you to work inside the mouth as well, especially on the bars.

Be careful here to not hurt the tissue. Most of the muscles of the mouth and lips attach to soft tissue. You'll want to do more of a wake up touch in the mouth than try to release adhesions.

Find the respiratory rhythm of the horse, by watching the nostrils flair, and work to it by moving gently and slowly through the mouth.

You may want to wet your hands to better match the moisture of the tissue inside the mouth.

Don't forget to work the lips all the way around, top and bottom.

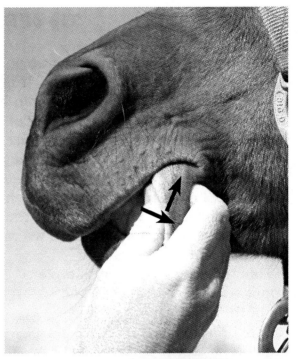

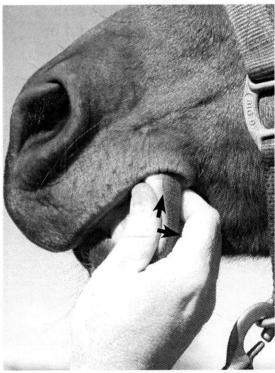

Figure 15 A and B *Mouth Work*

Nose Work

The nose should feel flexible not hard. Can you imagine that a horse might be holding tension in its nose? Besides that possibility it is important to work this area to: complete the fascial release of the head and to bring the awareness of the horse to this area. **Figure 15**

The technique here is a combination of c stroke, circles and skin rolling. Be careful when you are working near the cartilage of the nose, don't mistake it for an adhesion and try and get rid of it.

When you are over the top of the teeth, in the lower portion of the nose, don't apply too much pressure downward. In fact there's no need for much pressure at all, go slowly and stay at an even depth.

With this type of work it is best to work a little and stop and let the horse process what you've done. If the horse likes it or is at least receptive to it they'll stay around for more. If not they'll try and leave. Giving them the opportunity to leave lets you know how much they can take of this type of work, and lets them know that it will stop. This is much better than forcing more of what they don't like on them.

I find that this type of work asks a lot of the horse in that

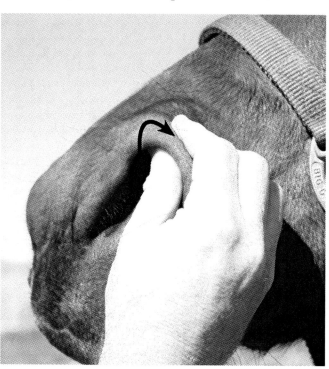

Figure 15 *Nose Work*

it is providing them with many new sensations. Because of this, they may not be able to process the input into their nervous system as easily as work in other areas. With that in mind, keep a close eye on how much time you are spending here. Less is often better.

Chapter Contents

Techniques for the Neck

120   Equine Structural Integration: Myofascial Release

Muscle Name	Origin	Insertion	Action	Figure Reference
Nuchal Ligament	Withers	Occiput	Supports Head	**1 and 2**
Nuchal Ligament Lamellar Section	Withers and Nuchal Ligament	Cervical Vertebrae	Supports Cervicals	**1 and 2**
Rhomboid	Occiput	Medial Scapula	Lifts Scapula	**4 and 5**
Brachiocephalicus	Occiput and C1	Humerus	Flex Humerus Sidebend head	**3**
Serratus Ventralis	Cervical 3-7	Medial Scapula	Raise Thorax	
Scalenes	First 3 ribs	Cervical 4-7	Raise base of neck	**3**
Complexus	Cervical Vertebrae	Nuchal Ligament	Raise neck	**4**
Splenius	First 3-4 Thoracics	Occiput and first 5 cervicals	Bend Neck and extend head	
Sternocephalic	Sternum	Mandible	Extend head, turn head	

Table 1. *Muscles of the Neck.*

Nuchal Ligament Bending

The *Nuchal Ligament* provides support for the head—it allows the head to hang forward without muscular effort—as well as an attachment for neck muscles such as: Cervical Ventralis, Rhomboid, Splenius...

The nuchal ligament is subjected to a torque from the muscles that attach to it. It can also develop cross links with the myofascia of these muscles.

The *Bending* Technique **Figure 1**, helps to break up these muscular cross links as well as cross links that are internal to the ligament itself.

This technique is just as it describes, bending the ligament as if you were trying to break a small stick—you would bend it one way and then the other way, back and forth, until it broke. This is exactly how your hands move to perform this technique.

Carry this bending along the entire ligament from both sides of the horse. Your thumbs are positioned in the *groove* between the ligament and the muscles that attach to the ligament.

This is a good technique to teach to your clients as an addition to their normal grooming.

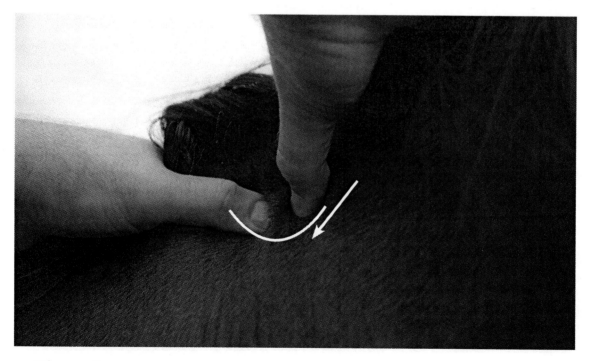

Figure 1 *Nuchal Ligament Bending*

Nuchal Ligament Distraction

The same *breaking-a-stick* analogy that was used in the bending technique is applicable here. If you follow that analogy one part is called bending and the other part is called distraction. It is really an arbitrary distinction whether you are bending or distracting.

The arrows in **Figure 2** indicate that the thumbs are separating while the ligament is being bent towards the therapist. The the real work is being done by the fingers on the other side of the horse's neck. As in the bending technique you work up and down the ligament.

If I get to a part that is particularly adhered, I'll grab hold of the ligament and give the entire thing a gentle shake. Horses try to break up the adhesions in the same way when they shake their neck. They don't have the mechanical advantage to put the energy into the ligament and give it a cross link disrupting shake that we do. (Of course this is pure conjecture on my part. They may be shaking their neck because they have fleas!)

When you are done with this technique, it is a good idea to follow up with an *organizing stroke*, either towards the head or the withers.

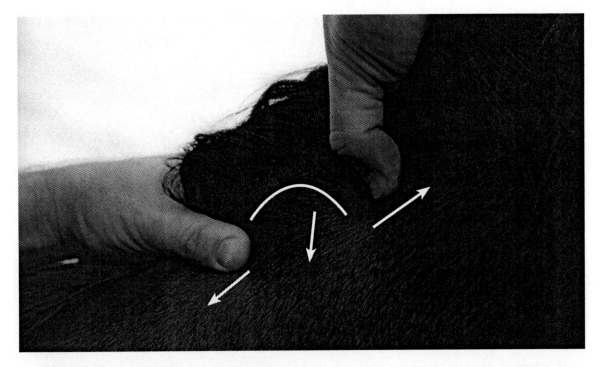

Figure 2 *Nuchal Ligament Distraction*

Brachiocephalicus Sweep

The *Brachiocephalicus* muscle is one of the "work horses" of the neck. Not only does it move the head from side to side, it is a prime mover (*protractor*) of the front leg and as such is primarily responsible for upper arm *extension*. The brachiocephalicus works in conjunction with the *latissimus dorsi*, which also attaches on the humerus. Reduction of length in this structure will result in: shortened stride, a head that cannot come to vertical, and a head not able to move evenly from side to side. The head may be *tilted to one side* if one brachiocephalicus is shorter than the other—with the nose tilted away from the shortened one. If it is hypertonic it can constrain the *scalenes* to prevent *neck telescoping*.

The sweep, **Figure 3** is a deliberate slow grabbing of the fascia while taking it down towards the humerus. Taking the tissue down is not important; it is just easier than taking the tissue up because the location of the cervical spine's transverse processes.

Be mindful of the *jugular vein* in this grove.

To help have the handler bend the horse's head toward you to put slack in the muscle. Watch for the neck telescoping to occur as you work this structure, that is a good sign that the scalenes are working. As you approach the scapula be mindful of the *nerves* of the *brachio plexus!*

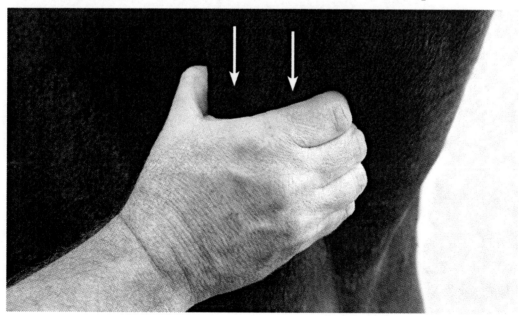

Figure 3 *Brachiocephalicus Sweep*

Rhomboid/Splenius/Complexus Sweep

The three muscles named in this technique, occupy the same relative space, but at different depths. You really can't work on one without working on the others.

The rhomboid starts at the cranial (toward the head) border of the scapula and attaches along the nuchal ligament. The splenius is below the rhomboid going from the thoracic vertebrae and the nuchal ligament attaching on the cervical vertebrae. The complexus is below the splenius going from the nuchal ligament to the cervical vertebrae and is inscripted with a tendon between each of its segments. A complicated anatomical arrangement that allows for a lot of neck movements.

In **Figure 4** the sweep is towards the head along the inferior (lower) border of the rhomboid at the depth of the complexus. You can see the fascia in front of the elbow below the skin almost taking on the shape of the complexus.

This work should result in a neck that has more depth from throat to crest. When you do your standing analysis of the horse, you should gauge whether the horse's neck is proportionate with the rest of the body.

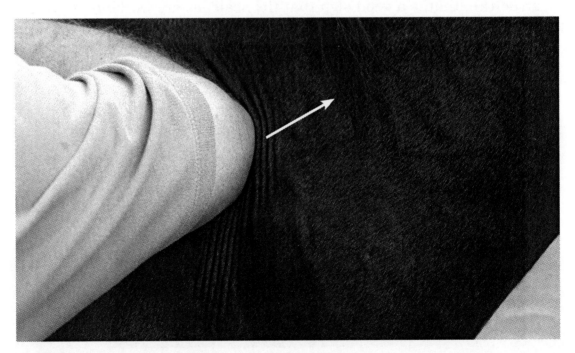

Figure 4 *Rhomboid/Splenius/Complexus Sweep*

Rhomboid Knuckle Sweep

The *Rhomboid* works in conjunction with the *Serratus Ventralis* attaching on the superior cranial border of the scapula. (The top towards the head border of the scapula) Often a horse that is *cinchy or girthy,* has a problem in the rhomboid as well as the serratus ventralis. The rhomboid can often contribute to a shoulder restriction that will not allow the shoulder to move laterally during forward thorax motion. (Remember the shoulder has to move out of the way of the thorax for collection to occur.)

The scapula is *slung* between the rhomboid cranially and the serratus ventralis, ventrally. This is very similar to the brachiocephalicus/latissimus dorsi arrangement. The rhomboid can eccentrically resist the scapula movement of the serratus and vice versa. (There are three main variations of contractions in muscles: eccentric, concentric and isometric.)

The Rhomboid Sweep shown in **Figure 5** is along the inferior border of the rhomboid, moving toward the shoulder. Direction to sweep is determined by tissue testing. Above the hand is the cervical portion of the *Trapezius* which is addressed in a scapula technique.

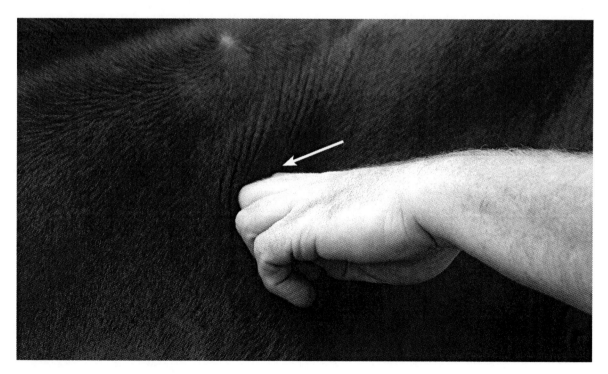

Figure 5 Rhomboid Knuckle Sweep

Chapter Contents

Techniques for The Shoulder

Muscle Name	Origin	Insertion	Action	Figure Reference
Trapezius Thoracic Portion	Thoracic Spine	Spine of Scapula	Raise Scapula	**2**
Trapezius Cervical Portion	Spine of Scapula	Cervicals	Bring shoulder forward	**6**
Supraspinatus	Scapula, cranial to Scapula Spine	Humerus	Protract Humerus	**2, 5, 7**
Infraspinatus	Scapula, caudal Scapula Spine	Humerus	Protract Humerus	**2, 5, 7**
Latissimus Dorsi	Spine and Lumbar Aponeurosis	Humerus	Retract Humerus	
Serratus Ventralis Thoracic Portion	Ventral Ribs	Medial Cranial Scapula	Depress Scapula, Raise Thorax	
Rhomboid Thoracic Portion	Cranial border of Scapula	Spine	Raise Scapula	

Table 1. *Muscles of the Shoulder*

Shoulder Skin Rolling

This skin rolling technique, **Figure 1**, is very useful as a diagnostic and for releasing fascial adhesions of the scapula.

The muscles of the scapula are organized in a number of *fascial compartments: infraspinatus, supraspinatus* and *trapezius.* These fascial compartments can adhere to each other crossing the scapular spine. The spine will feel like there are soft bumps on it when this happens. These muscle are also subject to a lot of compression and micro trauma due to saddle fit, movement and position.

You can start the skin rolling anywhere on the scapula and go in any direction you like.

Using this as a diagnostic, if you find a restriction you can decide whether you want to use a different technique to address it. As a release technique you would continue to skin roll moving your thumbs, and therefore your emphasis, each time you make a pass over an area.

In **Figure 1** the skin rolling is happening with the fingers feeding tissue into the thumbs. The adhesions, if any, will be felt between the fingers and thumbs.

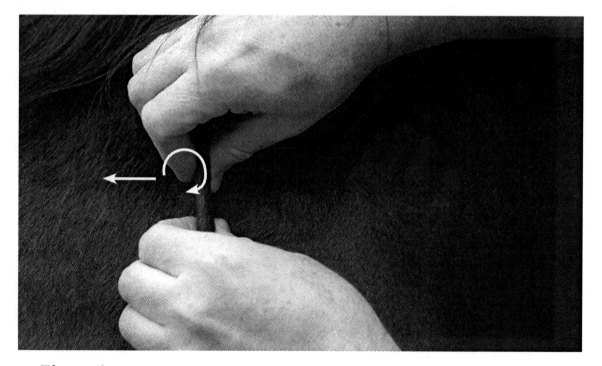

Figure 1 *Shoulder Skin Rolling*

Shoulder Compression

The shoulder compression shown in **Figure 2** is a very effective way to release a large sheet of fascia. Take the entire superficial fascial layer into compression and hold it until you feel an overall release of it. Then slowly withdraw from the layer. You should see a difference in the tissue ease as well as a change in scapula position as the top of the scapula—white arc—moves laterally away from the withers.

The white line between the hands indicates the *scapula spine*. On the right is the supraspinatus and on the left the infraspinatus.

After releasing the superficial layer, which contains both, you can go a layer deeper and individually release these two structures.

The bunching of the skin, in this figure, is where the trapezius fascia is.

This is often one of my first few strokes on a shoulder. It provides me enough fascial length to perform the more detailed techniques.

It is also a good idea to go back to this stroke, after having done more detailed work, to release layered restrictions.

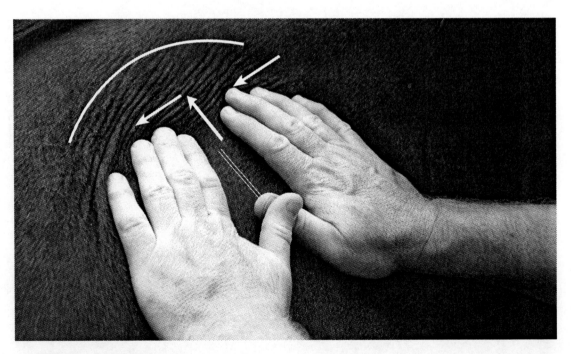

Figure 2 *Shoulder Compression*

Sweeping the Scapula Border

Once you have enough slack in the scapula's fascia you can sweep its cranial border. In **Figure 3** the fingers have followed the bone around the border of the scapula to work with the subscapularis. The thumb is on the cranial portion of the scapula spine (the white line).

You work the subscapularis in this way. If its rolled over into the supraspinatus' space you can clean it off the border. In other words you would make more of a distinction between the subscapularis and the supraspinatus. You can also bring the supraspinatus back into its space if it has rolled over the scapula border.

Once your fingers are around the border you can work the tissue up and down. Keep your finger pressure lateral into the scapula to avoid closing the space of the brachioplexus. If the horse acts irritated you may be increasing the pressure on a nerve. Remove your hand and try again, perhaps with the horse's neck being bent towards you.

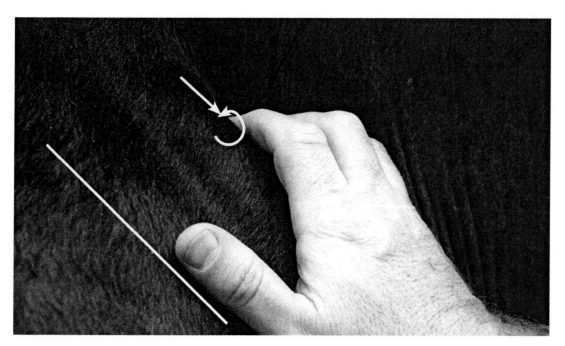

Figure 3 *Scapula Border Sweep*

Scapula Border Sweep

You can use this technique to do more detailed work on the border of the scapula.

It is very important that the scapula is able to move easily within the fascia that encases it, and that the layers of fascia (superficial and myofascia) are able to slide relative to each other. If these fascial layers are "glued" to each other the front limb will not be able to move freely.

In **Figure 4**, the left hand is not working. The right hand's index finger knuckle is being used but the whole back of the hand could be used as well. Engage the fascia and slowly sweep it up or down along the border of the scapula.

It is important that the wrist be straight while doing this type of technique, for two reasons:

1. the transfer of the force is easier, and the ability to pickup sensation from the hand is enhanced

2. if the horse should decide to move its considerable weight into you, it won't be through just the wrist but through your entire arm.

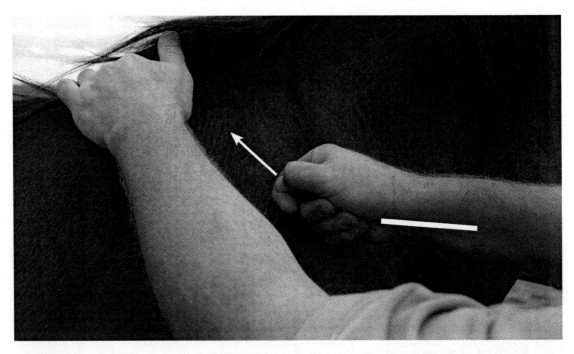

Figure 4 *Scapula Border Knuckle Sweep*

Scapula Spine Sweep

The scapula spine, the line in **Figure 5**, should feel like a bone, not like bubble wrap. Just as in the case of the tissue rolling over the cranial scapula border (described earlier), the separation between the supraspinatus and infraspinatus can be compromised at the spine. I think this happens with saddle usage and the movement of the scapula under it.

In the figure the tissue is being taken up the spine of the scapula by the index finger in the infraspinatus' space. You could take it the other way just as easily. Move slowly, this can be a tender area. You can also "wake up" this area as you work, with the horse having a reaction to the sensation. Often horses have become numb here due to improper equipment fit.

When you've done one side of the spine (infraspinatus in the figure) you'll want to work the other side as well (supraspinatus in this case).

The right hand in the figure is not working but marking the end of the spine and the beginning of the scapula cartilage.

Wrist position is important here for the reasons mentioned earlier

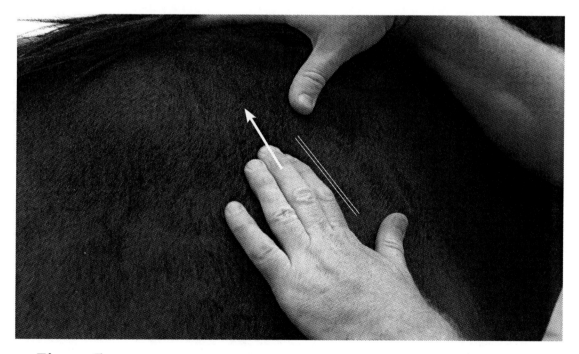

Figure 5 *Sweeping the Scapula Spine*

Cervical Trapezius Barrier Hold

Working on the top of the shoulder the Trapezius is engaged in **Figure 6.** Tissue test the trapezius fascia to determine the direction of least *ease,* this is the barrier.

The first fascial tissue barrier is held until it releases. Once the first barrier releases the next one, if there is one, is engaged and held in a similar manner. The fingers are pointing towards the rear of the horse or in a *caudal direction.*

The trapezius is like a cape, covering the top of the shoulder with attachments on the scapula spine and fascia. The trapezius is identified as two muscles—the thoracic and cervical—based on the relative location of their origin on the nuchal ligament. The saddle sits on top of the trapezius and often impedes it in its movement of the scapula—the cervical portion moves the shoulder forward and the thoracic portion moves it upwards. It is also often adhered to the fascial layer below it, like it was flattened.

The fingers in figure 6 are engaging the trapezius fascia caudal to the scapula spine.

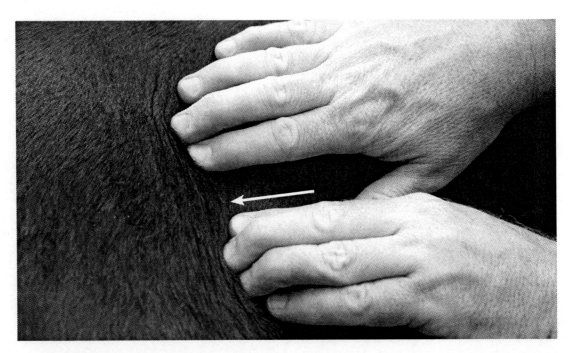

Figure 6 *Trapezius Barrier Hold*

Scapula Spread and Hold

This is a very good *integration* technique. It can be used to re-organize the superficial fascia after working on deeper layers. **Figure 7** shows the technique as a spread and hold. The thumbs are being used, which I advised against, you could just as easily use your knuckles, fists or elbows.

The key point with this technique is to contact the layer of fascia that you wish to work with using both hands. Next spread the hands and the fascial layer to the first barrier and to hold it until the barrier releases. Proceed to the next barrier and hold it.

If you slip off the layer with either hand start over.

When you've removed the barriers in one plane move your hands, down or up and start again. You can make the move, down or up, large or small, there's no guideline. The arrows in **Figure 7** give some idea of how far apart one could make each stroke.

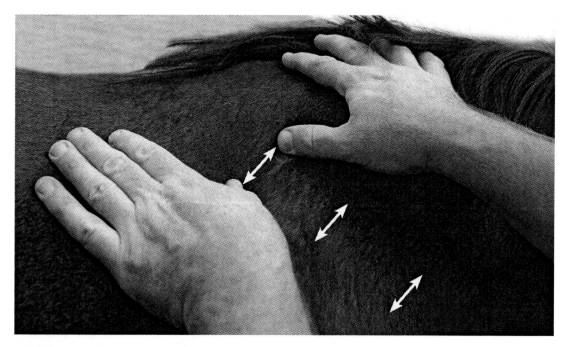

Figure 7 *Scapula Spread and Hold*

Subscapularis Release

This technique is wonderful for providing space between the scapula and the thorax. While I call it a subscapularis release, **Figure 8**, it does much more than only release the subscapularis. It creates the space for the scapula to easily move over the thorax by breaking adhesions between the subscapularis and the thoracic fascia. It works the attachments, fascia, of the serratus ventralis and the rhomboid. The intention is different than the previous scapula border sweep as is your body position. You are now positioned more in front of the horse.

The technique is performed by slowly sliding around the cranial border of the scapula and working the subscapularis.

Before you can do this technique you'll need to open the Trapezius fascia. This will provide you with enough tissue length to reach around the scapula. **Figures 6 and 7**.

While performing this technique make sure to keep your fingers on the subscapularis to avoid entrapping the brachioplexus. If you feel something hard at the tips of your fingers that may be a high first rib. If you do encounter the first rib, it may be held high by the scalenes, release them.

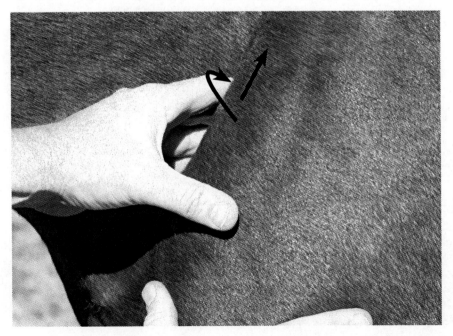

Figure 8 *Subscapularis release*

Chapter Contents

Techniques for the Forearm

Muscle Name	Origin	Insertion	Action	Figure Reference
Ascending Pectoral	*Sternum*	*Upper Medial Humerus and scapula*	*Adductor and Retractor of Humerus*	**1**
Descending Pectoral	*Sternal Manubrium and Ribs*	*Medial Humerus*	*Adductor and Protractor of Humerus*	**1**
Transverse Pectoral	*Caudal portion of sternum and ribs*	*Medial humerus*	*Adduct humerus, raise the thorax*	**1**
Latissimus Dorsi	*Spine and Lumbar Aponeurosis*	*Humerus*	*Retract Humerus*	**4**
Triceps	*Caudal border of scapula*	*Elbow (olecranon process)*	*Flex Shoulder and extend elbow*	**2, 3**
Rhomboid Thoracic Portion	*Cranail border of Scapula*	*Spine*	*Raise Scapula*	

Table 1. *Muscles of the Forearm*

The Forearm

The forearm, as used in this text, is defined as the Humerus and the Radius/Ulna and their associated soft tissue. The effects of the soft tissue imbalances originating here will be seen throughout the leg and foot. Many of what we call *conformational faults* of the front limb can either be corrected or mitigated by our work here.

The axial skeleton (body) is suspended between the two front limbs—which can be thought as a two flexible posts—which make contact with the ground as the body moves.

The front limb is also required to act, in a limited way, as a shock absorber. The quadrupeds's forearm is not evolved to absorb shock, the rear limb, with its angulation is better suited to this task. (Watch a horse coming over a jump and you'll see how the front limbs reach out to absorb the shock. Unfortunately the horse did not evolve to jump and the stress of shock absorption on the front of the horse puts a huge burden on the structures of the feet and the thoracic sling muscles.)

Because of the length of the front limb the soft tissue forces acting higher in the leg will be magnified lower in the leg and foot. A small change in rotation higher in the leg (this distance is called the *lever arm*) will create a greater torque (Latin for "to twist") lower in the leg (the applied leverage).

An example of this occurs every time we open a door. The door is attached to hinges that allow it to move. We apply a force (that is much less than the weight of the door) to the door at the door handle, which is at a distance from the hinge. The force we apply is transmitted and magnified through the rigid door to the hinge which causes the door to open using much less force than the door weighs. (Weight is a force.)

This same physical principle is applied when working with the legs. If you see a rotation in the leg, in standing or in movement, look further away for a larger rotation. If you don't see one, then the initial rotation you saw is caused by a smaller deviation further away. (The lever arm "magnified" the force.) Working on this place, that is causing the rotation, will get results; while working directly on whatever you initially saw, will not.

Here's an example: You see a horse with a laterally rotated leg—it toes out—with a foot flight pattern that matches. The large deviation is in the foot's flight, while the causal rotation is smaller and higher in the leg. If the causal rotation is in the foot than the leg will exhibit an even larger rotation higher up. Working on the smaller rotation at the origin of the lever arm will have tremendous effects farther away.

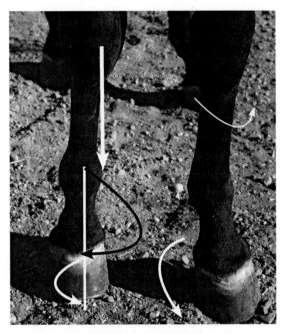

A small rotation higher in the leg will exhibit as a larger rotation lower, in the foot, because of the leverage principle. (Left leg)

The same principle applies for the rotation that will occur in the fetlock and foot caused by the offset between the long and short pastern bones. (Right leg) The weight is offset coming through the joint (white arrow). There will be a counter rotation at the short pastern and coffin bones.

Conformation

While this text is not a conformation manual, there are some things to look for before you start to work on the forearm:

The leg should be clean with no swelling. The leg should be straight, as viewed from the front, with no crooked lines .

It should be cool to the touch. Run your hand down the leg to the top to the hoof, there shouldn't be any soft boggy spots in the tissue. There shouldn't be any heat in the joints or tendons. A horse that is being used hard may have wind puffs which are distensions of the synovial lining of the fetlock. These indicate wear in the joint but are not a problem if they are cool to the touch. Heat means a repair is underway and is a contra-indication for fascial release.

Pick up the foot and see how balanced it is. Move the fetlock joint, is the movement easy or feel restricted? Many horses have restricted fetlocks since they stand and work on flat surfaces all day. Moving this joint will help to distribute the synovial fluid. Look at the hair along the inside of the foot at the coronet. Is it intact or cut? A horse that toes out will have a hoof flight pattern (like the photo above) that brings the two feet close together cutting the hair on the opposite foot.

Holding the leg at the fetlock let the foot hand down while you site down it. Is it dropping straight down or deviating to one side or the other? If there's a shoe, are the nails evenly worn on both sides of the shoe? Are there cuts on the heel, from the rear feet contacting it?

Looking at the leg from the side as the horse weights it, is the leg completely in extension or stuck between extension and flexion? Are the flexor tendons going through the carpal retinaculum cleanly or are they *tied in at the knee*?

Often horses that have a tight carpal retinaculum will not be able to come back into full extension. This pre-disposes them to stumbling on that leg when it is weighted. You can release this fascia to help the horse that stumbles.

Safety and Body Mechanics

Working on the front of the horse presents some interesting challenges with precautions to take. Horses strike with their front legs as well as stomp at flies, both of which can hurt if you're on the receiving end. I like to put one of my feet on the foot of the horse while working, this warns me when that foot is moving. (That is at least three times I've written that!)

Our body mechanics present another challenge when working here. To do some of these techniques you'll have to either bend over or kneel on the ground. If you are bent over and the horse moves you could strain your back getting out of the way. If you are kneeling you could be knocked down. This is a place to be very careful, to work slowly and to take a lot of breaks to stand up and stretch your body. If you start to get tight the horse will respond by getting tight. Taking care of yourself is also taking care of the horse.

When you bend over make sure you come back up from a straight neutral position. In other words if you've bent over and moved your torso sideways, come back to straight before you come back up. This will bring your spine into neutral mechanics and prevent your getting stuck.

Before you get in front of a horse or bend over near one, make sure you survey your environment both the physical and the human. Can you move safely away from the horse in all direction? Are there flies, other horses, cats, dogs, people feeding/working around you that may distract the horse? Is the handler present with you mentally or distracted by the environment? You are responsible for your safety!

Pectoral Sweep

The Pectorals make up the majority of the *thoracic sling.*
You can start this technique by putting your hand on the sternum
and following it back towards the rear. Feel for any tissue buildup on
the sternum, it should feel like a bone with a thin fascial covering on it. You
should clean it off by slowly engaging the tissue and taking it laterally.

Also note any lateral deviation in the sternum; where it feels like it is
pointing to one side or twisted, this will indicate possible spine or rib issues.

The Pectoral Sweep shown in **Figure 1** takes the pectoral fascia both
laterally and caudally. You start this by slowly differentiating the pectoral
from the sternum. You then take the pectoral (the descending shown here)
and work it slowly down towards the arm. You'll feel the tendon long before
you get to the arm; you should work it as well. Take your time here, horses
don't get touched here often and they may react to it. Or, they may just say
thanks! Stay here until you feel it has released, and then work the other
side of the horse, immediately to maintain balance.

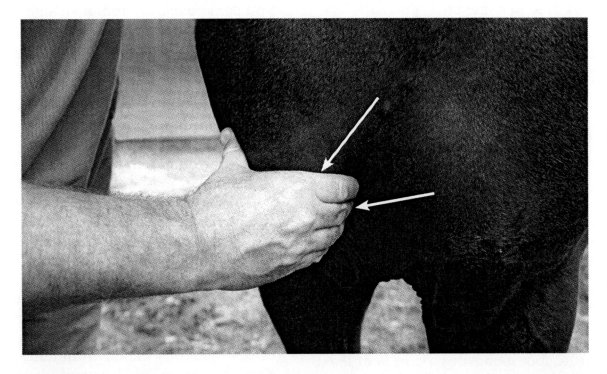

Figure 1 *Pectoral Sweep*

Triceps Attachment

The *triceps* attaches to the *ulna.* The tissue in this area can feel confused; the technical term is *gonked up.* **Figure 2** Any time that you are working with an attachment at the bone, the bone should feel like a bone and not soft tissue. Clean the tissue off the bone as needed both medially and laterally.

The triceps attaches at the *cranial border* of the ulna with the three *heads* lining up across it. If the triceps is stuck in contraction it will tend to rotate the ulna and by extension the *radius* since they are fused. This, even slight, rotation will be reflected in the foot's flight pattern. To effectively work with the caudal portion of the long head of the triceps you'll have to work from the medial side.

Slowly sink in between the radius and the ulna and take the tissue to the rear, to create more space for the joint to operate. This should result in a more extended protraction.

Figure 2 *Triceps Attachments*

Triceps Sweep

Once you've cleaned off the ulna portion of the triceps you can feed more length into the body of it. The intention here is to create more space in the myofascial container.

In **Figure 3** I am moving the tissue down. The elbow is marked, in the photograph, for you to have a reference point. Start up at the scapula and work down into the tendon's attachment on the bone.

At some point you'll have to move to the front of the horse to be able to effectively engage the tissue from the cranial border of the scapula.

While you are working here you may want to assure that there isn't more tissue buildup occurring on the ulna. To do this you can alternate between this technique and the last one.

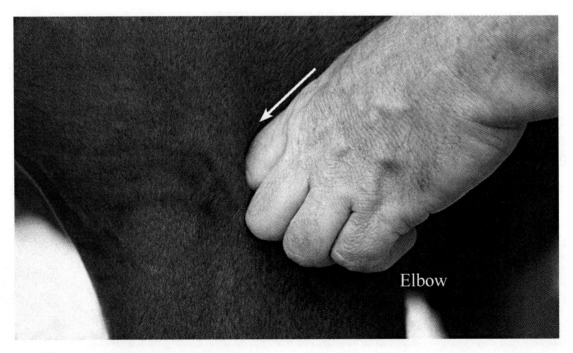

Elbow

Figure 3 *Triceps Knuckle Sweep*

Latissimus and Triceps Separation

The Latissimus Dorsi, has to pass under the triceps on its way to the medial side of the humerus. (The triceps occupies the lateral edge and the latissimus the medial one.) The myofascia of the two muscles can become *glued*, another technical term, to each other. Actually, cross links can form between the two causing the latissimus or the triceps to drag the other along when they contract.

To perform this technique you have to be able to feel for the individual fascial borders or *septum* that separates these two structures. Once you've found the border between them, use cross fiber friction to break apart any adhesions.

Figure 4 shows a localized compression of the latissimus to re-hydrate it and breakup any adhesions that may have formed. The palm of the hand is resting on the triceps while the fingers are moved caudally until I could feel the border of the triceps and the latissimus under it. It feels like you are rolling off one muscle on to the other, with the triceps border having more distinction. You could also approach this from the opposite direction.

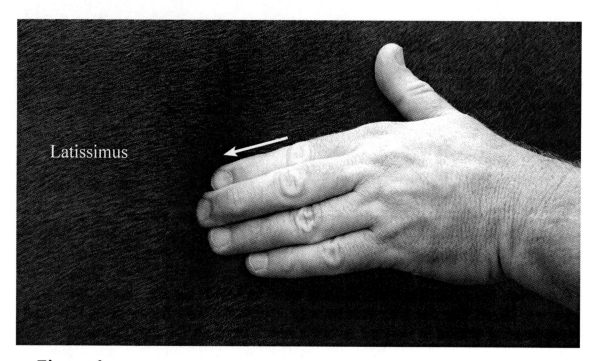

Latissimus

Figure 4 *Separating Triceps and Lattisimus*

Serratus Ventralis Release

The serratus ventralis is often involved in horses that are considered *cinchy.* It is easy to understand why, since it lies under the cinch. One of the problems is the buildup of tissue in an attempt to stop undue motion in the muscle's fascial sheath. This tissue buildup has been coined a *false retinacula,* by Louis Schultz. **Figure 5**.

The tissue buildup has to be removed for the serratus to completely contract and lengthen. The lack of length effects the shoulder's ability to completely flex as the serratus inhibits the cervical rhomboid. The primary causes of cinchiness are:

1. A congenital pre-disposition to being shorter on one side. Perhaps from the way the horse laid in the womb.

2. The movement of the girth (white arrows) on the tissue itself.

One of the common problems that occurs with a cinchy horse is that the owner/handler becomes sensitized to the horse's reaction and stops working the area, even when grooming. This leaves the tissue set in this pattern, and actually reinforces the pattern.

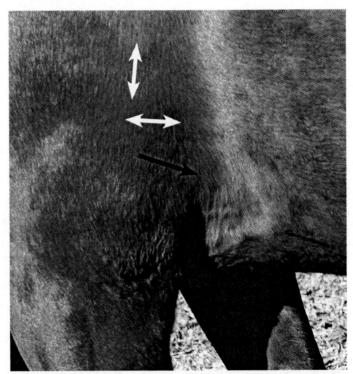

Figure 5 *The Serratus Ventralis False Retinacula.*

The cross fiber friction technique is used to break up the tissue buildup. **Figure 6** Much like the scar treatments. Once the tissue has been released an organizing stroke is needed to set a new direction for the fibers. Stretching the leg will also help. (Bring the foreleg backwards, shoulder flexion, to effect the serratus' tissue.)

Serratus Ventralis Release, continued...

The therapy for this can't stop here though. The girth issue needs to be addressed for a long term solution to cinchiness to be complete. This may have been caused by a simple problem with equipment or a long term one of the rider being off balance while riding.

Mounting from a mounting block will help. Mounting from both sides of the horse will help. Of course riding balanced will help. If the client is cinching very tight because their saddle is slipping to one side this is a good clue that they are riding off balance or that their saddle doesn't fit the horse.

I'm not a saddler or a riding instructor so my advice here is limited. I do suggest to my clients that they use a tool called a *Grooma* in this area to continually break up the cross links that may develop.

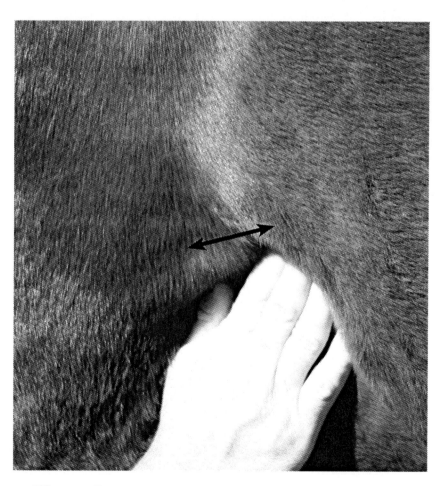

Figure 6 *Serratus Release*

Chapter Contents

Techniques for the Rear

Muscle Name	Insertion	Action	Figure
External Intercostal	Between Ribs	Moves ribs in inhalation.	1
Longissimus Dorsi	Vertebra from Sacrum to neck.	Extend spine, bend spine.	2
Lumbar Aponeurosis	no insertion	Acts as an attachment and spring	3
Middle Gluteal	Greater Trochanter of the Femur	Abduct hind leg and extend the hip	4
Gluteus Maximus	Greater Trochanter of the Femur	Abduct hind leg	4
Bicep Femoris	Femur; Patella; Tibia and Hock	Extend hock and stifle, retract femur	4
Semitendinosus	Stifle, Tibia and Hock	Flex Stifle and hock, retract femur	7
Semimembranosus	Femur	Retract and adduct femur	5
Quadratus Femoris	Lessor Trochanter of femur	Retract and rotate femur	5
Adductor Magness	Femur and Tibia	Adduct, rotate femur	
Tensor Fascia Latae	Fascia Lata	Protract femur	
Quadraceps Femoris	Patella	Extend Stifle Protract femur	

Table 1. *Muscles of the Forearm*

The Ribs

Assuring that the ribs are free from restrictions will help to increase lateral bending. The two main places where lateral bending occur is in the neck and the thorax. The thorax bending is limited by the rib's ability to move and the space between them. The horse has 9 - 11 *floating ribs*—ribs that don't attach to the sternum.

The *rib cage* moves in compression and extension with the action of an elastic component made up of the intercostal muscles and fascia. In breathing the ribs act like a "venetian blind" moving in and out at an angle. Ribs can become stuck in either the "in" or the "out" movement and become painful. They also have a "bucker handle" motion of up and down at the spinal attachment. (If you sense your client has a rib problem refer them to a veterinary chiropractor for an adjustment.)

The rib cage is covered with superficial fascia, almost like a tarp covering a stack of hay. You'll need to open this before you can work on the intercostal's myofascia. To open the superficial fascia contact it with both hands spread over a broad area and engage any restrictions to movement over this big *sheet*. It is not important to work on small spots you might find, take a larger view to working with this superficial fascial sheet.

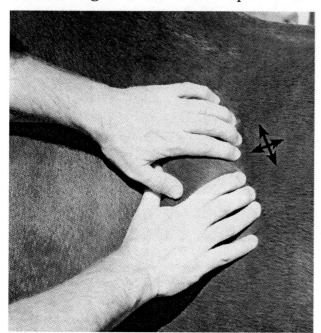

Figure 1 *Rib work*

To work with the external intercostal fascia, palpate the ribs and slip in between two of them. Go slowly taking the tissue either downwards or upwards or both **Figure 1**. The nerve innervating the intercostal is found in between the ribs. Time your movement to the respiratory pattern of the horse. The tissue will relax on the exhale.

To avoid nerve entrapment go slowly and softly. After you've worked a couple of ribs, step back and see how the horse is breathing where you worked.

Spinal Erector Compression

The spinal erectors have to be able to *Span* between the withers and the lumbars. The term span is one that Ida P. Rolf, PhD. used to describe the action of two ends moving apart in soft tissue.

When we watch the horse trot or canter we want to gauge the ability of the longissimus to span, rather than contract. If the muscle seems to be popping up with every stride, it is not spanning, and needs to be released.

The technique, **Figure 2**, is accomplished by sinking into the tissue lateral to the erector group (the entire group is worked rather than one individual muscle's fascia).

Once you've sunk to just above the ribs and transverse spinous processes, compress the tissue medially towards the spine. As you encounter a barrier hold it until it releases. When you get too tired or can't find another barrier, slowly come back away from the spine. (The guideline is to take twice as long releasing as you did compressing.) This allows time for the nervous system to adjust to your departure, and to take on the role of supporting the tissue as you leave. If you leave too quickly, you'll risk creating a *rebound effect* where the tissue will rebound back to its old holding pattern. Do this technique moving down the entire spine to the lumbar aponeurosis.

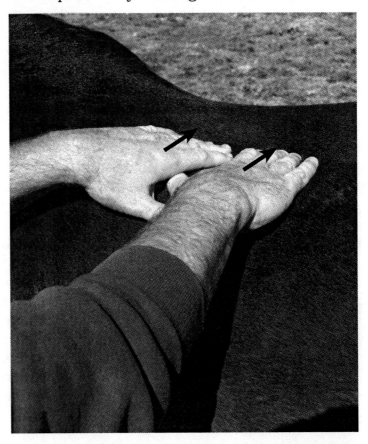

Figure 2 *Longissimus Dorsi Compression*

Erector Sweep

Once you've finished with the erector compression you can follow it with an erector sweep to re-organize the tissue along the spine. There are six layers of myofascia in this area. Each layer is deeper or closer to the spine than the one above. Each spinal erector muscle has a job of moving and stabilizing the vertebra. The most superficial layer will move more than one spinal segment while the deeper layers only move one vertebra relative to its closest neighbor.

This sweep is best done from above the horses back, with you standing on something such as a mounting block. Get your body weight behind your elbow and use the flat part of the elbow, not the pointy end.

As you sink into the tissue you'll feel it release in front of your arm. Follow the release to the end. You don't have to use one stroke to cover the entire back.

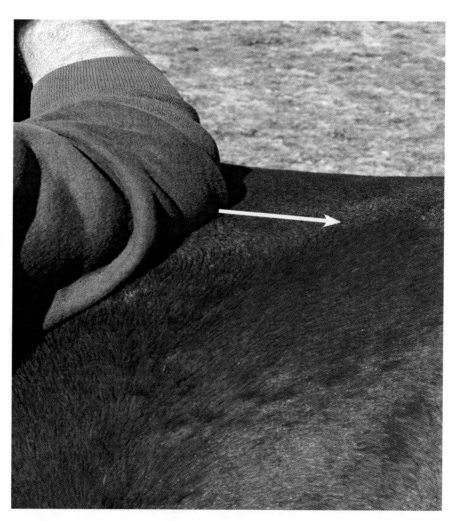

Figure 3 *Erector Sweep*

Lumbar Sweep

The lumber area is a place where tissue confusion can occur. The main soft tissue structure in this area is the *lumbar aponeurosis* (the white box indicates a part of it) which is both an attachment point for many muscles, and a soft tissue *spring*. As a spring it stores energy from the pull of the muscles during *lumbar coiling* to release later in the stride. The ability of the horse to coil its lumbar region is directly related to the extensibility of the lumbar aponeurosis.

This sweep, **Figure 4**, is best done with the elbow. Not using the *pointy* part of the elbow but more the long part of the ulna bone. The hand should be relaxed to not transmit tension into the tissue. The angle is down and out away from your body, with your body weight used to apply the pressure. There is no muscular effort required on your part just let your weight work for you. To help with this you may want to stand on a mounting block.

It is important that you use your weight and that the movement is away from your body; not using your pectorals to pull across your body. This pulling could eventually lead to an entrapment of your thoracic outlet and neck strain.

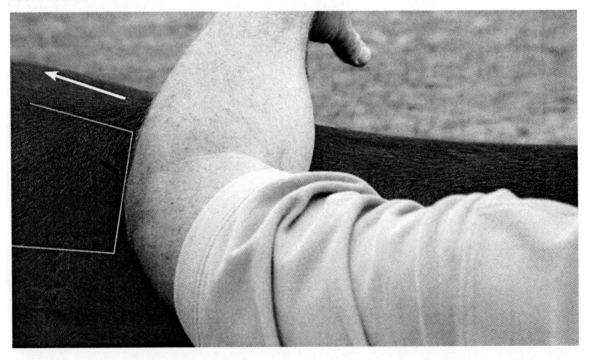

Figure 4 *Lumbar Sweep*

Gluteal Compression

This technique, shown in **Figure 5**, starts by releasing the superficial fascial sheet. The arrows in the figure are a little misleading. They should go straight into the page, showing the pressure going straight in towards the body.

Start this technique with your two hands contacting the largest *sheet* of fascia you can while still maintaining the fascial feel between the hands. Lean your body weight into the fascia and sink until you engage the first barrier; hold there for the release and then sink in to the next one and so on. When you are done, slowly withdraw from the tissue. If you withdraw too fast you'll cause a rebound effect in the nervous system, and perhaps create more tissue holding as a response to your leaving.

You can vary the angle that you are taking the tissue—in, up, down—as you need to. Be sure to use good body mechanics, leaning in to use your weight. Try to keep your wrists aligned with your arms to transfer the energy efficiently and to avoid injury if the horse should suddenly move.

Take breaks and watch for the horse's breath to move through this area.

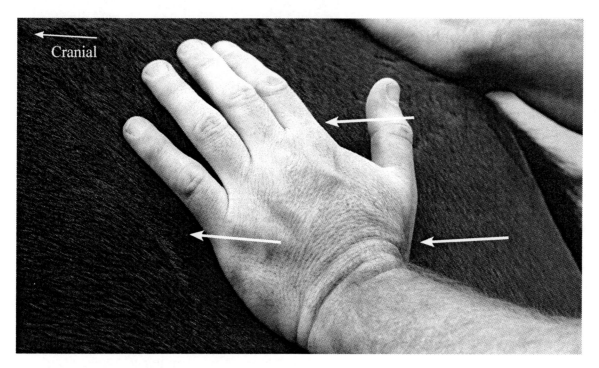

Figure 5 *Gluteal Compression*

Bending of the Semimembranosus

The semimembranosus is the most medial of the hamstrings. Its fibers rise up into the sacral fascial bed and lumbar aponeurosis. As such it can be involved in sacral subluxation. The technique shown in **Figure 6** is great for breaking up cross links and increasing the tissue length.

It is also a beneficial technique for separating the fascia of the semimembranosus from that of the semitendinosus.

This technique is performed like all of the other bending techniques in that the bending is done in two directions. (Like you are breaking a green stick.)

There is another problem that is common with the semimembranosus; it will develop an adhesion at the level of the *Tuber Ischii.* This adhesion feels like a lump that dissipates with direct pressure. The technique that one can use for this is called *Ischemic Compression. Ischemia* is a lack of blood in soft tissue; the compression on the tissue causes the blood to be pushed out along with old metabolites and waste products. You release the compression slowly and then re-compress the tissue, literally pumping out the old fluid and bringing more blood and nutrients into the tissue. (This is like the the exercise you did with the sponge.)

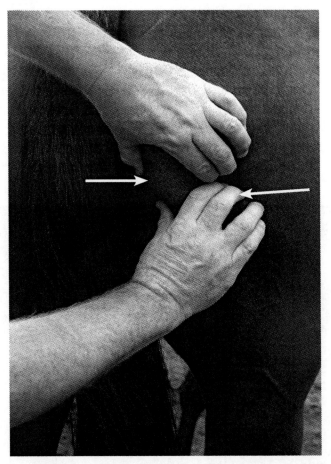

Figure 6 *Semimembranosus Bending*

I have found these adhesions to be as big as a walnut. They can also be hard or feel like a scar. Returning this tissue length to the hamstring will increase the rear leg forward stride; enough that they can pull front shoes if you didn't open the front first!

Semimembranosus Sweep

A s in any of the sweep strokes, this one is great for providing more organization to tissue, as well as bringing length and better hydration. **Figure 7** shows the direction the forces are applied—in to the tissue and down the hamstring.

This technique is used for the semimembranosus, rather than the knuckle or fist, because you are working around the tuber ischii and the fingers are more sensitive. Once you've cleared the bones you can switch to knuckles, fist or elbow.

You'll want to stand outside of the horses kick zone when you do this. In case you activate something uncomfortable for the animal.

You'll also want to start as high as you can, making sure you get the tissue close to the tail, and separate the semimembranosus from the *Levator Ani.*

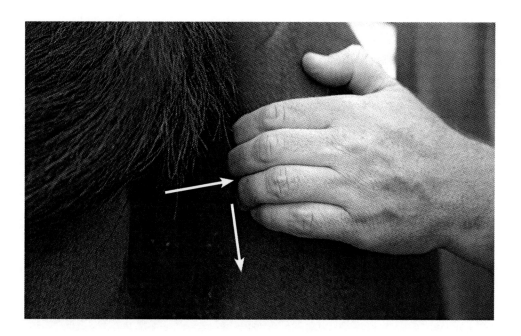

Figure 7 *Semimembranosus Sweep*

Semitendinosus Sweep

The Semitendinosus attaches into the sacral fascial bed and can contribute to sacral subluxation. This is especially true of horses that jump—a *hunters bump.*

The *sciatic nerve* is running down the back of the leg here. You want to be aware of this nerve so you don't compress it. The sciatic nerve is the largest nerve in the horse's body. You should try and gently palpate the sciatic nerve, to get a feel for it.

Figure 8 shows the angle of the stroke; in slowly and then downwards. You might want to tissue test to see if the fascia wants to go up instead of down. The starting point for this technique is just below the *point of the butt* or *tuber ischii.*

It is always a good idea to stand off to one side when working here, near the sciatic nerve, since it may provoke a kick. Most of the time the horse will try and sit on your hands, moving their body to help you.

It is important that you have good body mechanics at all times while working here, since the horse may move unexpectedly.

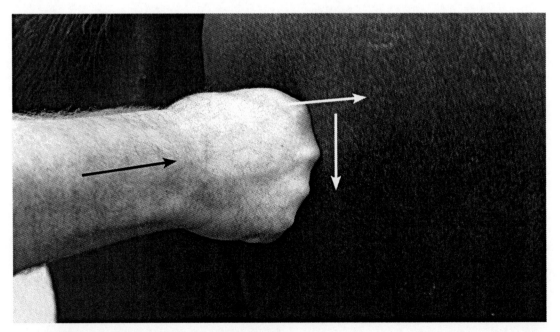

Figure 8 *Sweeping the Semitendinosus*

Semitendinosus Compression

The semitendinosus compression, **Figure 9,** is used to integrate the fascia of the rear of the horse, especially the sacrum and the tail. The semitendinosus has fibers that control the lateral movement of the tail. If you see a horse with a tail carried off to one side you'll want to release this muscle and fascia.

Obviously, while performing this technique, you are standing behind the horse. This isn't a problem but to be on the safe side hold your body as close to the horse as you can without compromising your body mechanics.

As you push into this tissue you'll see the sacral bed rise and flatten, black arrow, this is a good sign and an indicator of how free the fascia is.

The fascia here usually feels like a trampoline. You'll have to enter slowly, as usual, and wait for the wave of softening to precede your hands. You can use another tool, fists, elbow ... if you like, I just happen to be using my hands. Use your body weight not your arm muscles!

You can help free the tail by bringing the tail over to one side and working the opposite side, the convex side, to lengthen the tissue there. Then reverse the bend and work the other side.

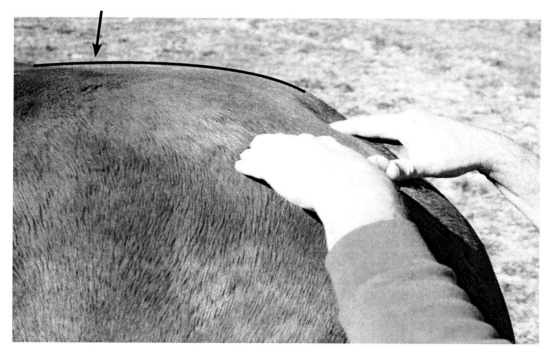

Figure 9 *Semitendinosus Compression*

Lumbar Compression

The lumbar compression, **Figure 10 A and B**, is similar to the semitendinosus compression, only coming from the opposite direction. Its purpose is to lengthen, hydrate and integrate the lumbar fascia and aponeurosis.

Many of the muscles of the back attach to the lumbar aponeurosis. When they are not balanced it puts a shearing strain on it. If this strain is not relieved or organized (as Rolfers like to say) it has to the potential to set up twisting forces throughout the body. (Imagine laying in bed with the sheets wrapped in a twist, the tension from this is transferred to your body, or you wouldn't feel it! Now you know where "big sheet work" as an idea comes from.)

Take the Latissimus Dorsi (LD) as an example. It attaches from the lumbar aponeurosis into the humerus. If the attachment point of the left LD has a different spacial relationship than the right one, a twist will be introduced into the body when the leg it protracted. (The brachiocephalicus will be encountering two different resistances as they move the front legs forward. This lack of balance could set up a twist in the neck.)

Notice the difference in the back, in the two photos, when the hand is just laying on the back and when the aponeurosis is being engaged. (The black lines, line up with the top of the tree in the background as a horizontal reference point.) You should see this same type of engagement of the aponeurosis when the horse is moving. If you look closely, at the photo, you will also see that the gluteals are softening.

The end result of using these last techniques is a more balanced aponeurosis and a relaxed back.

When watching the horse move, the hips should move independently up and down, as the rear leg swings under them and into the stance phase. (The rear end shouldn't move laterally around the midline of the body which indicates a resistance in the back.) The front leg should have a greater reach as the Lattisimus Dorsi more easily extends. The back should be able to rise, and then rest back into a more rounded frame as the energy stored in the aponeurosis is released. Working here will help to achieve this.

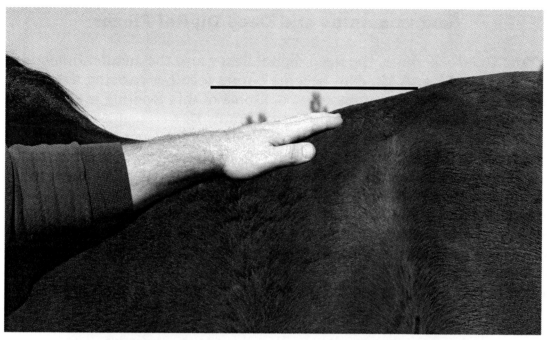

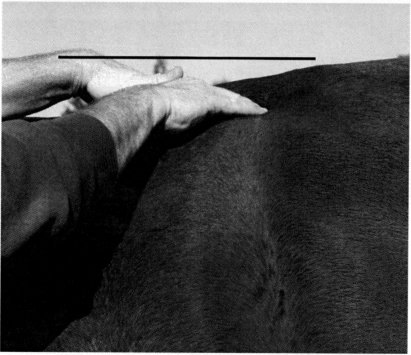

Figure 10 A and B. *Lumbar Compression and rounding*

Gastrocnemius and Deep Digital Flexor

The Gastrocnemius, the deep digital flexor and the semitendinosus, **Figures 11 and 12**, can become bound together causing the twisting at the rear leg we commonly see. (Some of this twisting is attributable to the *screw home* effect of the tibia and femur. However, if it is excessive, look to these structures as the cause. Remember the lever arm effect!)

This area is frequently disorganized. What you are trying to arrive at here, is a separation of the myofascial compartments, to allow them to hydrate and slide relative to each other. You want to feel for the edges of the muscles and make sure they are distinct from one another.

The tibial and peroneal nerves are in this area so don't pin anything to bone. It is a good idea to work from the medial side of the horse, and watch out for a cow kick.

I had to risk my life to get the photograph for you! You don't need to.

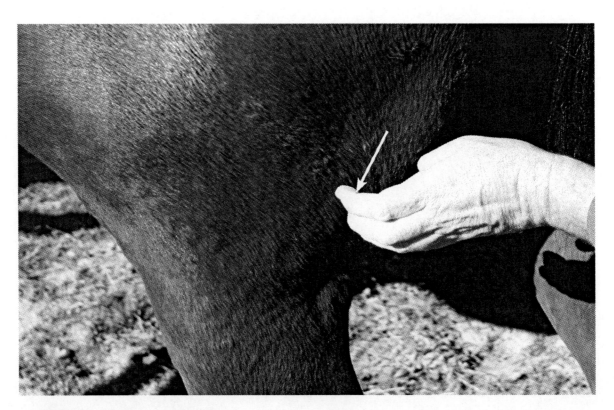

Figure 11 *Gastrocnemius*

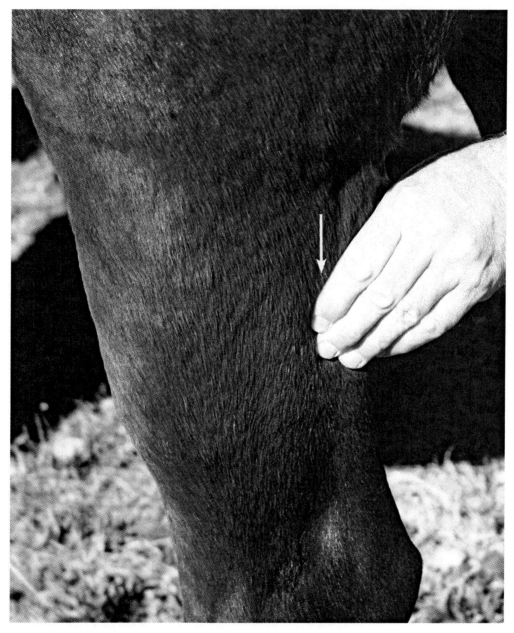

Figure 12 *Gastrocnemius and Deep Digital Flexor*

Biceps Femoris Separation

This area, **Figure 13**, is another one that has potential for a lot of confusion and myofascial adhesions. We want to assure the biceps femoris and the lateral head of the gastrocnemius are not tied together causing a rotation in the leg with movement. Similar to the last technique you are working on the separation of the myofascia as well as on the biceps femoris itself. The biceps work is done with a sweeping stroke.

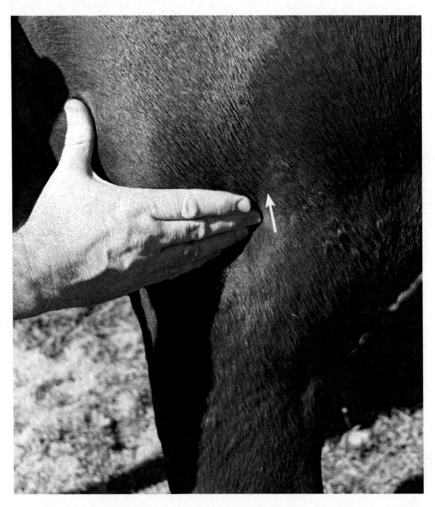

Figure 13 *Biceps Femoris and associates*

Tensor of the Fascia Latae Compression

The Tensor of the Fascia Latae (TFL) is a prime flexor of the femur at the hip. It is as important in quadruped hip flexion as the quadraceps is for a human. It originates at the *point of the hip* or *tuber coxae,* a very important junction for many muscles, and attaches at the fascia lata a fascial sheet that encapsulates the patella (kneecap).

The technique, **Figure 14**, both engages the edge of the TFL while at the same time taking the tissue down towards the attachment at the fascia lata.

If this muscle is dis-organized it can pull the fascia lata laterally which will pull the patella out of its track. This can contribute to a locking or sticky patella. The black arrow points to the patella. (The patella moves within a "groove" in the femur. If there is any lateral deviation to the pulls on the patella, from the fascia lata, the patella can be shifted out of the grove. When you touch the horse's patella it should not be painful. (Touch your own and see if it hurts.) A painful patella is indicative of imbalance.)

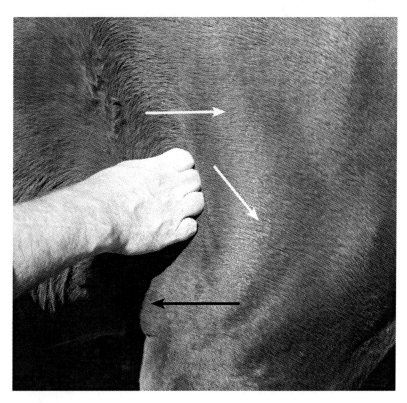

Figure 14 *Tensor of the Fascia Latae*

Adductor Sweep

The adductor technique brings an integration into the rear legs. It is not too often that therapists will release the potential in the adductors. Since we've released the abductors we now have to release the adductors to assure tissue balance.

The technique, in **Figure 15 A and B**, is shown in two stages:

1. The adductor fascia is engaged with the palms flat, this is a slow sinking process. This area is often sensitive to both male and female horses, including geldings. The fascia here is right below the skin since there's not much fat. Take your time sinking into the fascia which will mean bringing your hands towards your body, as if you were hugging the leg. Start as high as you can inside the thigh, being aware of nerves and blood vessels. Once you have tissue tested and have an idea how you want to take the tissue, you're ready for the second part.

2. Take both of your hands apart and engaging the restriction between them. I like to think of this move as the same as spreading a sheet on a bed or Rolfing table. You're taking out the wrinkles. The movement is in two directions, towards your body and out away from the midline of the leg.

Continue these two actions down the leg into the attachment lower on the femur.

A

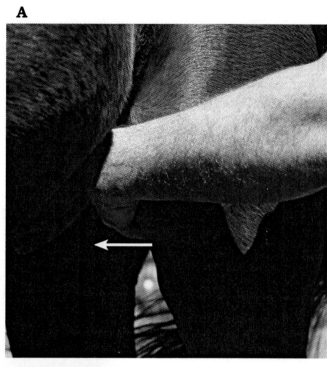

B

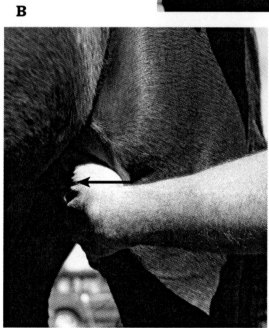

Figure 15 A and B *Adductor Sweep*

Tail Compression and Sweep

This technique, is not tail stretching, it is tail compression with a sweep. **Figure 16** The fascia of the tail, is right below the skin. Engage this fascia and slowly compress it, while at the same time taking it towards the end of the tail.

After this initial stroke, you can start to address each of the vertebrae in the tail by slowly taking the tail through its range of motion:

Side bend it.

Bend it up and down.

Put a slight rotation into it.

The white arrow points to a flattening in the semitendinosus that would clue me to work here. The muscle should look round, not flat, in this area. I would look for an adhesion on the medial side of the tuber ischii. The adhesion will feel like a lump. To work it, use Ischemic compression, where you pump the fluid slowly into and out of the adhesion. Releasing this will increase the stride length of the rear leg. Follow with an organizing stroke down the hamstring.

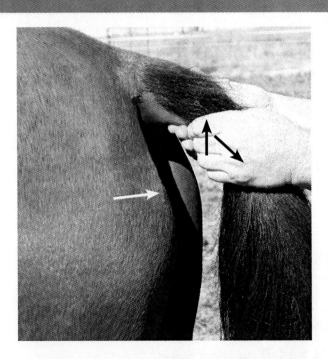

Figure 16 *Tail Compression and sweep*

Chapter Contents

Techniques for Scars

Scars

Scars are a special type of tissue adhesion in two ways: they are usually the result of some trauma and their lack of organization can be more disruptive to the body's movement than other adhesions.

Scars are an adaptation to injury. Normal healthy tissue has the ability to heal itself. The new tissue that is created in response to the injury is not always as strong or flexible as the tissue it replaces.

This lack of strength and flexibility occurs when the cells laying down the new tissue are not organized to lay their product down along the same lines of strain. The outcome is a network of collagen and elastin that is dis-organized. Cross links between the collagen do not allow energy to transfer along the line of strain. This allows the fibers to be continually disrupted during the healing process. In response, to make the tissue stronger, more collagen is laid down which reduces the overall elasticity of the tissue.

The therapy for scars depends on where they are in the healing process. For new scar tissue we need to be gentle to prevent disruption of the reticular fibers. In this case we want to supply an organizing force to direct the cells in laying down their product, while not disrupting it. If the scar has heat in it—it is probably still in the healing phase, don't work on it!

Using a TENS[1] machine can provide a gentle organizing force by causing the muscle to contract on a periodic basis. This works for scars that are early in formation and in either muscles or tendons.

For scars that are not in a place where a TENS can be used, we have to break down the cross links and manually add an organizing force. This is a long term project which you may need to teach to your client if the horse isn't yours. (The figures that follow show how to do this.)

Older scars that are colder than the tissue near them are a problem. The lack of normal temperature indicates they are restricted and need to be released.

When we work with the scar we want to break up the adhesions with four techniques: approximating, distracting, bending and cross fiber friction. After the tissue is free to move in all of its planes of motion we want to organized it with the use of the distracting technique.

Whether we are using the distracting technique as a means to break up an adhesion or for organizing depends on the intention we hold.

In general all of these techniques

are performed at the depth of the first scar tissue restriction. For older scars start at the superficial layer and work your way down as you open the tissue. Scars don't require much force. They do attention to the layer. You may find that you are doing these techniques using your finger nails to pick at the adhesions. Do what ever it takes but go slow and with specificity.

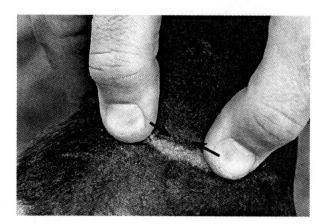

Figure 1 shows the scar being approximated—a fancy way of saying the ends are brought together.

As you can see this will only break up the adhesions in one plane of motion.

You may find a instance where this technique can be used to organize the tissue.

Figure 1 *Scar Approximating*

Figure 2 shows the distracting technique—another way to say "take apart".

While one thumb, the left, is anchoring the tissue, the other is taking it away. This only breaks up adhesions in one plane of motion.

You may find a instance where this technique can be used to organize the tissue.

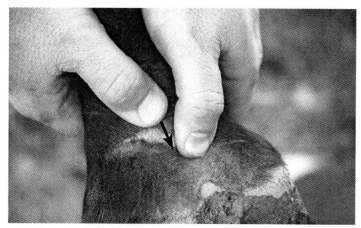

Figure 2 *Scar Distracting*

Figure 3 shows cross fiber friction. This is the oldest technique on the planet for breaking up adhesions. You may want to start out with this one to soften a scar.

The technique is applied as the name implies; you engage the tissue you want to disrupt and move across the grain of the fiber.

This technique will not substitute for an organizing stroke, no matter how good your intention is!

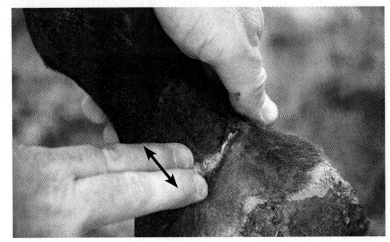

Figure 3 *Cross fiber friction*

Figure 4 illustrates the bending technique as it is used with a scar.

You find the layer you wish to be on and then bend the tissue taking the two, thumbs in this case, apart. As you've seen in the other technique sections I like to use the bending technique to break up adhesions on a large scale,

You could use this technique to break up adhesions in a flexor tendon if you were helping a veterinarian rehabilitate a bow in it.

This technique could also be used to introduce organization into the tissue.

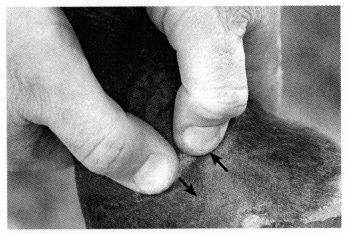

Figure 4 *Scar bending technique*

Scars worthy of mention

Some if the scars you will encounter in the horse are so common that we can describe protocol to use for working with them.

The most common scar is the gelding or castration scar. If you haven't seen a horse being castrated you may want to find a veterinarian that will let you tag along on their next outing it will help you understand what the horse is experiencing.

The critical determinant of whether this scar will be a problem is the how soon the horse went back to work after the procedure. The early movement of the horse is important to break up the adhesions. Too often the horse doesn't get worked or they don't work enough, and the scar tissue migrates from the site of the incision and binds the fascia of the abdomen. This causes the horse to have a short stride; primarily behind but the front can be effected as well.

To tell if a castration scar needs to be released check it for temperature relative to the tissue near it. If it is cold then it does.

The bending technique is the one you will use in this area, using one hand to start with and then, if the horse is comfortable, using two.

Take your time to end feel into the scar to determine how much it has spread. When you are determining this you may feel like the scar has spread throughout the leg and abdomen. I would suggest that you work a little, releasing some of the adhesions and then check again. You may have felt the restriction in the fascial web more than the scar itself.

Another common scar is one that starts as a tear in the semitendinosus. This hamstring tear is not uncommon in jumping and reining horses. Because the initial tear is not well organized when it heals the tissue strength is not great enough to prevent re-injury. Sometimes this results in the horse being grade one lame which means could mean a lay up. More often it goes unnoticed until the horse is grade three or more lame.

In this case the scar tissue becomes more dense as the injury — re-injury cycle continues and eventually the collagen is replaced by calcites laid down by osteoblasts, in other words bone is laid down in the muscle, *ossifying myopathy*.

This scar is best handled with the finger nail picking type of work; immediately followed by an organizing sweep and stretching of the leg.

Teach your client how to do these techniques.

Lastly, is the scar that develops in the semimembranosus that was described in the bending the semimembranosus technique as a edemic pocket. If this edema is not removed the body will lay down more collagen in this area in response to the tension on the tissue—similar to a bone spur.

This scar should be treated the same as the one above using the finger nails and immediately following up with an organizing sweep.

Contents

Myofascial Stretching

You are probably familiar with some method of stretching, either for yourself or your horse. I want to introduce you to way of stretching, that will improve the ROM of the horses you use it with. You may find this way of stretching to be new or you may already be familiar with it.

Before we start, we need to cover a little background Anatomy and Physiology of the *neuro-myofascial network*, to assure that we have the same vocabulary.

The Basic Locomotor System

All mammalian bodies have a the same basic scheme for movement, *locomotion*. The muscles cross joints between bones. The contraction of the muscle either flexes or extends the joint, with these two movements being opposite each other.

The muscles are arranged on either side of the joint, with flexors on one side and extensors on the other. These muscles are labelled as antagonistic to each other.

The muscles on the same side of the joint, i.e. extensors, are labelled as agonists to each other since they produce the same joint movement.

From the movement scheme of

things bones are pretty stupid, they have no control over where they go. In fact they are simply fascial bags, periosteum, filled with inert mineral salts. (In the larger view bones are much more complicated and alive.)

The muscles, aren't much more intelligent than bones, they are a fascial bag, myofascia, filled with an electrical jelly.

In a very simplistic model, this electrical jelly is hooked up to the nervous system by a *motor nerve.* The motor nerve is like an electrical wire that turns the muscle on like a switch that turns on a light. When the nervous system wants the muscle to contract it sends a signal down the wire and the electrical jelly contracts. The muscle contracting moves the bone it is attached to at the joint.

Muscles can only *actively* contract, let me repeat that; muscles can only *actively* contract. Therefore, when the nervous system wants the muscle to lengthen, it turns off the signal to it, and at the same time turns on the *antagonist* muscle causing it to contract. (The muscles are arranged in antagonist pairs across the joint.) When an antagonist muscle contracts it *lengthens* the muscle on the other side of the joint.

One problem with this control system becomes apparent when

a muscle doesn't return to its original length when the antagonist contracts. This can happen for any number of reasons. One of these is a *nervous system latency* that allows the muscle to retain some of its contraction. (In electronic terms this is called *hysteresis*.) With each contraction of the muscle there is a slight retention of that contraction which the antagonist's contraction can not remove.

This is where stretching normally enters the equation. We stretch the muscle to return it to its original length. At least that is the theory. In practice what happens is that we might be able to stretch the muscle to more closely approximate its original length. However, if there is still an electrical charge turning on the muscle, we won't be able to return the original length through normal stretching. (In this case normal stretching would be analogous to taking the light bulb out of the socket to turn off the light.)

Myofascial stretching differs from normal tug and pull type stretching. It helps turn off the nervous system charge to the muscle. Please read on.

Motor System Physiology

The body's basic muscle contracting unit is called a *motor unit*. (By now you have seen that the body has a great deal of redundancy built into it.) A motor unit is: the motor nerve (the electrical wire) and all of the **muscle cells** (jelly filled bags), that the particular motor nerve innervates. When a motor nerve turns on, all of the muscle cells it innervates contract with all of their contractile strength. This is called an *all or nothing contraction*. If the motor nerve is on, then its innervated muscle cells are in contraction. If it is off then they are relaxed and can be stretched.

A muscle is made up of many muscle cells and many motor units. If the muscle is required to do precise work, like the lips of a horse, than there are many motor units to allow for precise movement. In this case, one motor nerve innervates fewer muscle cells. If the muscle does imprecise work, such as the quadraceps, it is made up of fewer motor units, with one motor nerve innervating many muscle cells.

In other words, in a precision muscle there are a lot of nerves controlling few muscle cells allowing a precise contraction of the muscle's motor units. In a workhorse muscle there are fewer nerves and less control. (A general rule is that a muscle that crosses one joint is more precise, and a muscle that crosses more than one joint is not.)

When a muscle is activated there has to be a mechanism for turning off the antagonist. Otherwise the muscles will oppose each other, and prevent limb movement. This mechanism is called *reciprocal inhibition*. Reciprocal inhibition occurs at the motor unit level, not the muscle level, so motor unit one of muscle X inhibits motor unit one of its antagonist muscle Y. When motor unit one of X is on, motor unit one of Y is off.

Unfortunately there are times when the nervous system gets confused about who's on and who's off. In these cases we can get a motor unit in a muscle that is supposed to be off but is actually *locked on* (it is also possible for a motor unit to be *locked off*).

Normal stretching can not change this nervous system confusion. We have to involve the nervous system itself to sort out who's supposed to be on and who's supposed to be off.

When you look at the pictures of myofascial stretching you won't see anything that looks too different from normal stretching. The legs are picked up and look like they're being pulled to a new length. This is what most people think stretching is. However, in myofascial stretching the legs are picked up, but rather than being pulled to a new length, they are

This confusion can occur when a horse slips in mud or acts up when being shod.

If the horse is running in mud and slips the nervous system can be confused by the feedback it is receiving from its movement receptors in the joints.

Another example:

A horse is being shod with the farrier holding the rear leg off the ground. The horse decides to put the leg down pulling it back; but the farrier doesn't let go. The muscle spindles fire and the nervous system recruits more motor units than is usually necessary to move the leg, and "forgets" to turn them off.

It's fairly prevalent. In fact, if you have a horse that stumbles a lot this motor confusion may be the cause.

positioned at the first place of tissue resistance. The therapist then waits for the horse's nervous system to release this resistance before positioning the leg at the next point of tissue resistance. The feeling, for the therapist, is like the horse is pushing their leg into them. They are actively releasing their leg. For the horse, its a resetting of their nervous-motor-system to a non-contracted neutral state.

Why is this different? By holding the leg at the tissue barrier we get the active participation of the horse's nervous system, which resets its motor nerve.

More importantly by the therapist only taking the leg to the first resistance it doesn't cause a *muscle spindle fiber* to fire. (Muscle spindles are the nervous system's feedback mechanism informing it about how much stretch there is in the muscle. The spindle fiber prevents the muscle from being overloaded by reflexively recruiting more motor units.) If the muscle is stretched too quickly or beyond the tissue resistance, the spindle may fire and cause the nervous system to activate more motor units within that muscle. This causes a stronger contraction which is the opposite of what we want. Often this recruitment is hidden from the person stretching the horse's leg by the movement of another joint e.g., the shoulder rotates when the front leg flexor's spindle fibers fire—seemingly creating more length in the flexors. Rather than effectively stretching the flexors we just caused a compensation further away.

You can find a video of this technique on my web site www. equinesi.com.

> *The Australian army did a study on the efficacy of stretching and its effect on injuries in basic trainees. There were over 10,000 participants in the study—they had no choice—some stretched before a workout, others didn't. The results were disheartening for stretch fans, those who didn't stretch had fewer injuries than those who did.*
>
> *The only saving grace for stretching was that they used the conventional style of stretching and not what I've described here. ('A Randomised Trial of Preexercise Stretching for Prevention of Lower-Limb Injury,' Medicine and Science in Sports and Exercise, vol. 32(2), pp. 271-277, 2000).*

Foreleg Triceps Stretch

Start the stretch by taking the leg upwards and towards you until you reach the first tissue restriction or barrier. Stay at this barrier until the horse lets it go by relaxing the muscle. It will feel like they are pushing into you.

The black arrows in **Figure 1** show the direction to take the leg to put tension on the triceps. The black lines give a relative idea of how much stretch occurs after each barrier is released.

The leg is not being pulled, it is being positioned at the barrier, upwards and out, and held there until the release is felt. Once the release is felt the slack is taken up until the next barrier felt. The leg is held at the barrier until a release is felt..

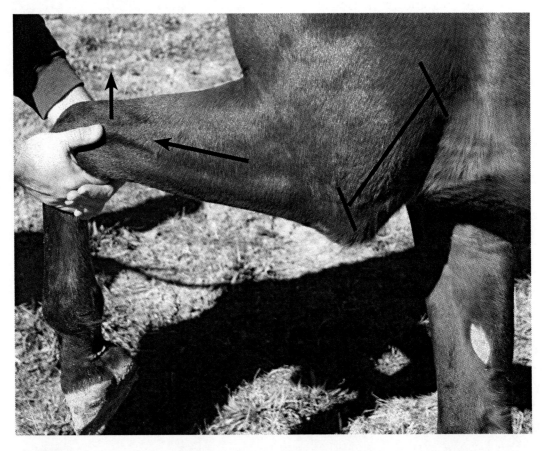

Figure 1   *Foreleg Stretch. Start the stretch by taking the leg to the first barrier.*

Foreleg Triceps Stretch 2

After the first barrier is released the leg is taken towards the therapist to engage the next barrier, **Figure 2**. The leg is held at this barrier until the leg releases.

Once again, this is not active pulling of the leg, it is held at the barrier waiting for the horse to relax/release into the new position.

Notice that the leg hasn't moved forward but that the elbow has dropped while at the same time the leg has become more horizontal, indicating a relaxation of the triceps.

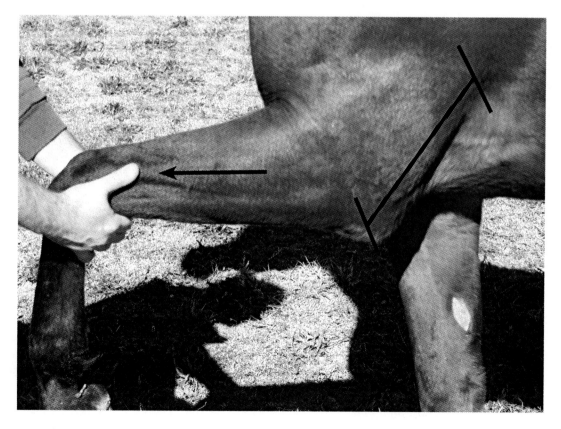

Figure 2 *The second barrier is engaged and held after the first release.*

Foreleg Triceps Stretch 3

I n this final release, the horse is pushing his leg out into the barrier rather than having it pulled out. The nervous system can reset and regain motor control over the muscle's action.

"Motor control over the triceps action" means that the motor system has turned off the motor units that were locked in an "on" position. The antagonist muscle can now fully contract.

You may also feel the resetting of motor units that were locked off. This will feel like small tremors or contractions with the leg being pulled slightly away from you. Motor control reset in general feels like a wobbling or shaking in the tissue. You'll see this in muscles that are coming back into use or whose use is being learned by the nervous system. Across joints this will occur when the one joint muscles regain control from the two or more joint muscles.

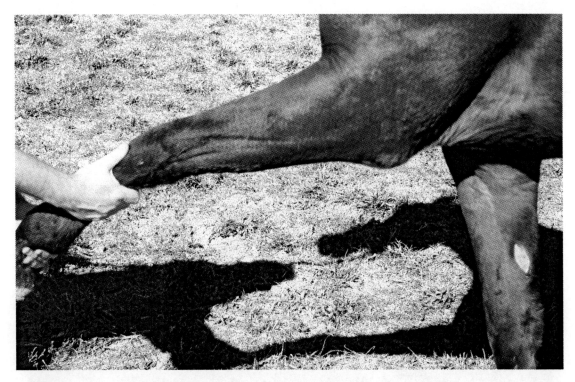

Figure 3 *The final release.*

Foreleg Deltoid Stretch

When you are done with the foreleg forward you can move around and take the leg to towards the rear. You don't have to put the leg down to do this. I usually do this stretch in the opposite order than is shown here when I am picking my horse's foot out. I'll do this one while I'm cleaning the foot and then reverse it to the previous one before putting the leg down. Using a verbal cue, like "stretch" seems to better connect the horse with what I am doing.

You've probably figured out that the technique for this stretch is the same as the first one: take the leg to the barrier and hold it. Then follow the release to the next barrier.

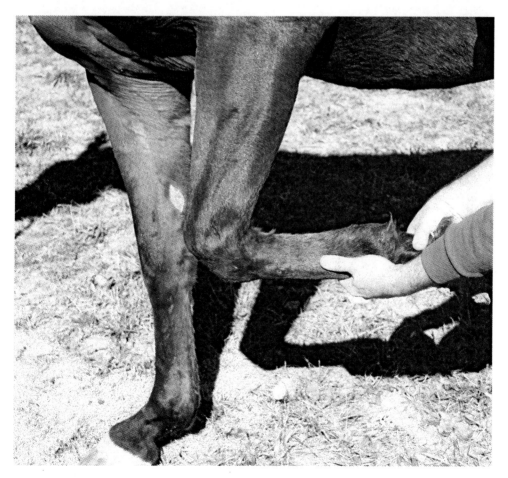

Figure 4 *Foreleg Back Stretch*

Rear Leg Hamstring Stretch

The next four figures show the rear leg forward stretch. The technique is the same as earlier: find the barrier and hold it there. Take up only the slack that is given, there's no pulling, rather the leg position is held until released. The release will feel like the horse is pushing into you. Be ready for the foot to extend past the front leg.

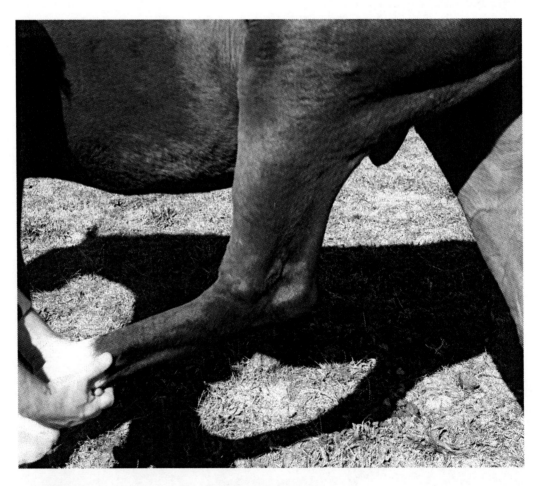

Figure 5 *Rear Leg Stretch First Barrier hold.*

Rear Leg Hamstring Stretch 2

The hock has dropped down. The second barrier is being held with out pulling on the leg. If the horse resisted and pulled the leg back I would let it have the leg and then slowly start over again. This kind of resistance often indicates a place where the motor system "thinks" it is going to experience a negative event. Taking more time and moving slowly to reset this, is all that is required. The reptilian brain pulls away from these assumed *noxious events*. Fortunately it doesn't have much cognitive capacity and will let go of the reaction fairly quickly.

Notice in **Figure 6** how far the foot has moved towards the front leg.

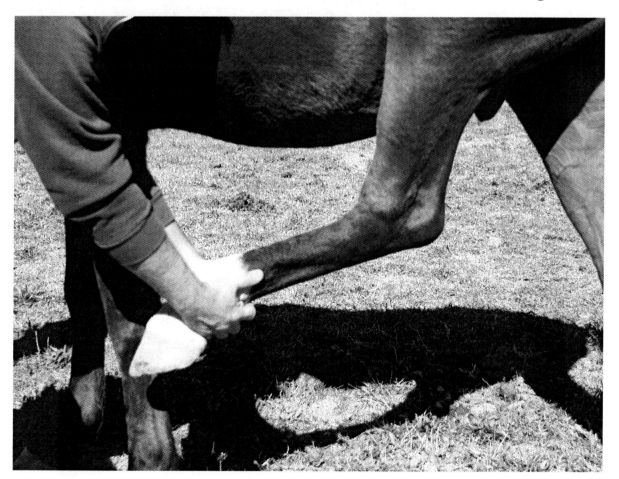

Figure 6 *Rear Leg Stretch. Second barrier hold.*

Rear Leg Hamstring Stretch 3

T he third barrier is engaged. The hands are cupping and supporting the fetlock. The leg is held at the barrier until the barrier is released.

These things that I've been calling barriers should not be confused with soft tissue adhesions. They are actually only a barrier in that the nervous system "thinks" that this is as far as the leg can go; the reset happens in the nervous system not the tissue. The nervous system program is reset by simply presenting a new sensation to it in a non-threatening way. If we were to pull the leg out to where we thought it should be we could threaten the system and re-enforce the holding pattern.

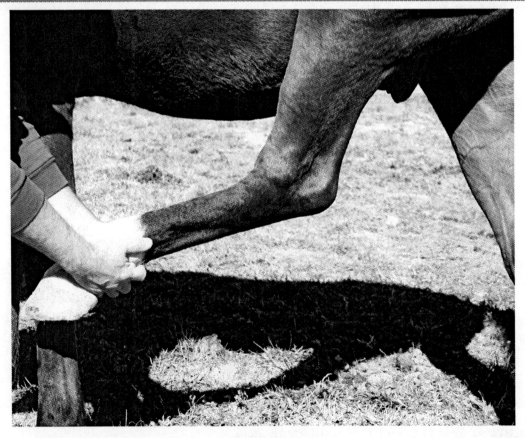

Figure 7 *Rear Leg Stretch. Third barrier hold.*

Rear Leg Hamstring Stretch 4

There is no pulling on the leg. The stretch comes from the resetting of the motor system.

Give this a try with your horse or dog or a friend. You can try this type of stretching on yourself, by taking your leg to a tissue resistance and holding it there while waiting for the release and the accompanying slack.

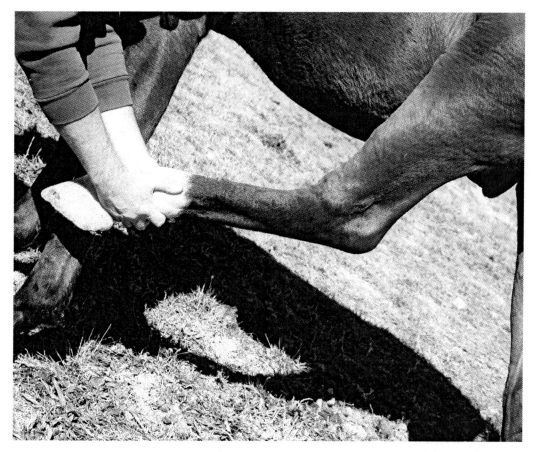

Figure 8 *Rear Leg Stretch. Fourth barrier hold.*

Rear Leg Quadraceps Stretch

Y ou can transition from taking the leg forward, the hamstrings stretch, to taking the leg back, quadraceps stretch, without putting the leg down. I usually start in this direction while I am cleaning the feet. As mentioned before, I like to use a verbal cue to help integrate this feeling into the horse's brain. I say "stretch" while doing this.

When I do this while cleaning feet, I rest the leg on my thigh. I don't like to bend over to work on the feet; when the horse can just as easily bring them to me!

Figure 9 *Rear Leg Back*

Working with Joints

To often joints are ignored in a stretching routine. This is unfortunate because the joint receptors provide the majority of the feedback to the motor system. In early chapters we talked about the problems that occur when a compressive force is not distributed over the entire joint surface. (Figure 8, page 25.) There is a possible wearing of the joint's hyaline cartilage, in the area where the force is borne.

Hyaline cartilage is avascular—it has very little blood supply—and depends on the compressive force to move waste products and bring in nutrition to the synovium.

Another issue that occurs with this off balanced distribution of force is that the nervous system receptors in the joint—which report to the Central Nervous System (CNS) the position and acceleration of the limb—will not be completely active. The receptors—pacinian corpuscles and ruffini end organs—are pressure sensitive and if not in line with the compressive force will stop reporting and be "turned off" by the nervous system. The result of this scenario is that the muscle motor units that are controlled by these receptors, now turned off, will also be turned off and putting more of a workload on the remaining motor units.

Taking this off balance compressive force one step further; horses who spend most of their time on flat surfaces will not have the opportunity to move the joints through their complete range of motion—which would normally be encouraged by uneven terrain. This lack of movement in the joint has to be countered with our stretching of the joint.

There are three movements that we need to encourage in the joint: compression, distraction and rotation. These three movements, done passively, will wake up the joint receptors, help to flush out metabolic waste products and increase the delivery of nutrients to the joint cartilage.

After years of boarding our horses, my wife and I bought our own acreage to keep the horses at home. The places where we had boarded had wonderfully flat pastures for turn-out, flat runs off the stalls and flat rubberized arenas. All of this was to prevent horses from having joint problems. When we got our horses home, I noticed that they were very sore after a couple of days in our undulating pasture. I realized that what was happening was, their new environment required their joints to move more, and that this was waking up long asleep motor units that were not used to the work. These now available muscle cells were sore from having to work again!

Joint Distraction

Before I describe this stretch, try an exercise: Stand up and weight each of you feet equally. Now lift one leg up and rotate the foot at the ankle, one way then the other. Stand on both again. Does one feel more alive than the other? Is it the one you rotated? This is the sensation of the joint receptors reporting to the CNS again. This exercise is combination of joint distraction—the weight of the foot distracted the joint—and rotation.

By doing this with our horses we will be: waking up the joint receptors, making available more motor units to distribute the muscular work load and increasing the health of the joint.

Joint distraction is a fancy way of saying, "pull it apart", when two ends of a joint are pulled away from each other they are distracted. When they are pushed together they are approximated.

What you are going to do here is gently and slowly pull the canon bone away from the pastern. You want to grip the bones, not the joint. Take the two away from each other, slowly, until you reach the end of range. The horse may sigh as it resets its nervous system.

When you have reached what you think is the end of range hold there for at least a couple of breaths by the horse and then slowly release the joint back into its normal length. Don't just let go of the stretch. To often people will do leg stretches with their horse where they distracting the fetlock and then they just let it go, plop, to the ground. This is problematic in that the

joint capsule could be "caught" in a distended position. We want to go slow to allow time body time to adapt.

Horse's spend so much time with their feet in compression that this distraction, de-compressing action is really a new and welcome experience.

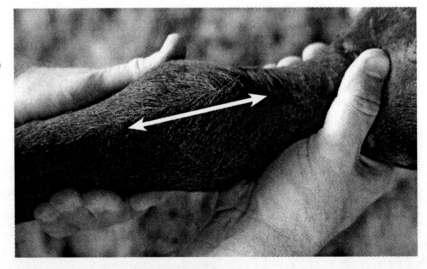

Figure 10 *Joint distraction*

Joint Compression

Compression is the opposite of distraction. Here we want to take the two bones towards each other. The other name for this action is "approximating".

It has been shown, in humans, that simply doing these two actions of distraction and approximating will help the recovery in people who have had joint surgery. It's these two actions that create the pumping action required to move the joint fluids.

What we are trying to do is not only move this joint fluid but also re-awaken the joint receptors.

Do accomplish this stretch you slowly and gently bring the two bones closer together—cannon and pastern bones. When you arrive at the end of motion, there's no more joint space, you can add a gentle rocking motion. Often the horse will sigh or even moan when you do this. You want to move slowly to allow the nervous system to process what's happening and to not alarm the horse.

Where letting go of the stretch too quickly in the distraction phase is potentially problematic, I don't think that is the case here. After all horse compress this joint all the time while walking or running.

However, this is not simply a compressing of the joint space, it is a compressing exploration of this space.

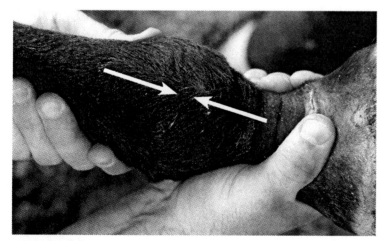

Figure 11 *Joint compression*

Joint Rotation

This is a combination of the last two stretches. The rotation starts by very slowly taking the joint through its available passive ROM. It's not important to increase the ROM while doing this, your intention is to wake up the joint. I like to do this whenever I clean the horse's feet. I have the fetlock and pastern joints readily Savailable on my thigh.

If I have the time then I will combine this with the last two stretches. So, there are actually three components to this:

1. With the joint completely passive and only a rotational component added by you. The rotation is as shown by the arrow.

2. You add a little distraction and explore the joint capsule's ability to move. When you add a rotation as well as distraction into the joint capsule it is important that you very slowly return the joint to the starting point. I suggest that before you do this you assure that your body position is comfortable for you.

3. Add compression and rotation.

You can also, move between these three to help move the fluid and wake up the joint receptors.

I continue these three with the joints in the foot. I haven't had much success with the joints above the fetlock. Mostly because of my body position being to awkward or comprimised.

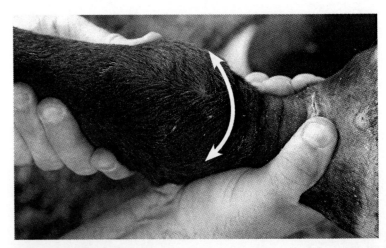

Figure 12 *Joint rotation.*

Bibliography

Budanski, Stephan. Nature of Horses. NY: The Free Press, 1997.

Chaitow, Leon. Palpation Skills. London: Churchill Livingstone, 1997.

Clayton, Hilary. Conditioning Sport Horses. Saskatchewan: Sport Horse Publications, 1991.

Dorrance, Tom. True Unity. Tuscarora, NV: Give-it-a-go Enterprises, 1987.

Equine Research. Conformation and Anatomy. Tyler, TX: Equine Research, 1999.

Grandin, Temple. Animals in Translation. Orlando, Fl: Harcourt Press, 2005.

Gray, Peter. Horse Structure and Movement. London: JA Allen, 1993.

Hunt, Ray. Think Harmony with Horses. Tuscarora, NV: Give-it-a-go Enterprises, 1991.

Ivers, Tom. The Bowed Tendon Book. Nunah, WI: The Russell Musdink Company, 1994.

Kamen, Daniel. The Well Adjusted Horse. Cambridge, MA: Brookline Books, 2001.

Lederman, Eyal. Fundamentals of Manual Therapy. London: Churchill Livingstone, 1997.

Myers T. Anatomy Trains. Edinburgh: Churchill Livingstone; 2001.

Nicholson, Nancy. Biomechanical Riding. Columbus, OH: Zip Publishing, 2006.

Oschman, J. Readings in the Scientific Basis of Bodywork. Dover, NH: NORA; 1997.

Paoletti, Serge. The Fasciae. Seattle, WA: Eastland Press, 2002.

Riegel, Ronald. Clinical Equine Anatomy and Common Disorders of the Horse. Marysville, Ohio: Equistar Publications, 1996.

Rooney, James. The Lame Horse. Hollywood, CA: Wilshire Book Company, 1974.

Rolf Ida, P. Rolfing. Rochester, VT: Healing Arts Press, 1989.

Schultz, Luis and Feitis, Rosemary. The Endless Web. Berkeley, CA: North Atlantic Books 1996.

Tellington-Jones, Linda, Bruns, Ursula. Equine Awareness Method. Milwood, NY: Breakthrough Press, 1985.

Travell J, Simmons D, Myofascial pain and dysfunction: The Trigger Point Manual. vol. 1. Baltimore: Williams and Wilkins; 1983.

Index

About the Author

Jim Pascucci has been working with horses since 1983. His first horse was an Arabian that he conditioned for use in competitive trail riding. From then on, until his son and he adopted a Peruvian Paso, he has owned only Arabians.

Conditioning and training his own horses he gained first hand knowledge of how difficult it can be to track down the reasons for the lack of performance improvement; or worse, the sudden decline in performance with no apparent reason.

In 1991 Jim left his engineering management position with Hewlett Packard with the idea of attending veterinary school. A bad horse accident at an endurance ride caused him to give up that idea. Wanting to do something with horses he was encouraged to become a Rolfer and work with horses.

Jim currently has a very satisfying human, equine and canine practice in Colorado and Bermuda, and is recognized as a pioneer in equine rolfing structural integration. He has made appearances on Fox Television's "Pet News", where he rolfed a horse live at the Chelsea Equestrian Center in Manhattan, NY. He has been featured on Colorado local news television as well as local and national print media. He has written articles on equine rolfing for equestrian magazines as well as the Rolf Institute Journal of Structural Integration and the International Association of Structural Integrators annual journal. (These articles are available at the web site www.equinesi.com).

Jim lives in Boulder County, Colorado with his wife, son, horses and the usual house pets. He conducts his equine myofascial release and structural integration courses at his facility in Colorado. (For more information on the course visit www.equinesi.com). To learn more about Jim and human rolfing visit www.jimtherolfer.com.

Lightning Source UK Ltd.
Milton Keynes UK

175600UK00006B/144/A